CHRIS·
IN·THE·
MORNING

CHRIS·IN·THE·MORNING

LOVE, LIFE, AND THE WHOLE KARMIC ENCHILADA

Compiled and Edited by Louis Chunovic
Based on the Universal Television Series
"Northern Exposure"
Created by Joshua Brand & John Falsey

CB
CONTEMPORARY
BOOKS
CHICAGO

Library of Congress Cataloging-in-Publication Data

Chris-in-the-morning : love, life, and the whole karmic enchilada /
   compiled and edited by Louis Chunovic.
       p.   cm
   Collection of observations mad by Chris Stevens, a character on
the television program Northern exposure.
     1. Northern exposure (Television program)   I. Chunovic,
Louis.   II. Northern exposure (Television program)   III. Title:
Love, life, and the whole karmic enchilada.
PN1992.77.N7C45   1993
791.45'72—dc20   92-47372
                                          CIP

Published by Contemporary Books, Inc.
180 North Michigan Avenue, Chicago, Illinois 60601
Manufactured in the United States of America
International Standard Book Number: 0-8092-3762-8

CONTENTS

ACKNOWLEDGMENTS

MY THANKS TO SOME OF THE COOLEST PEOPLE IN NORTH AMERICA, THE COLORFUL DENIZENS OF CICELY, ALASKA, AND THEIR WRITERS. WAY TO GO, EVERYBODY!

CHRIS-
IN·THE-
MORNING

INTRODUCTION

Joel Fleischman may be the town doctor, but the real healer in Cicely is the local deejay, a mostly easy-going, occasionally shaggy-haired young fellow named Chris Stevens. His loyal K-BEAR listeners throughout greater Arrowhead County, Alaska, know him as Chris-in-the-Morning.

Chris, a native of Wheeling, West Virginia (like John Corbett, the actor who plays him), is a self-educated intellectual who picked up his smarts on the street and his book learning in prison. While his New Age spirituality probably dates from the out-of-body experience he had one night in the joint after he "chug-a-lugged six hits of potato home brew while watching a strobe candle," Chris was blessed at birth with a strong curiosity about life, a healthy appreciation of the fairer sex (his own attractiveness is, as we learned in the episode entitled "Only You," a matter of fortuitous genetics—"the Stevens family pheromones," as he explains to Doctor Joel), and an eclectic ear for sounds.

And—oh, yeah—he loves to rap.

In the episode entitled "Brains, Know-How, and Native Intelligence" (the first episode to air after the pilot), Chris himself recalls for his listeners the exact moment he discovered the life of the mind. The book he's talking about, of course, is *Leaves of Grass,* by Walt Whitman, America's great poet of the senses and the human spirit:

IT WAS A DAY LIKE ANY OTHER DAY IN JOPLIN, MISSOURI, IN THE SUMMER OF 1976—THE AIR DAMP, THE SKY WHITE WITH HUMIDITY.

AND I, A BOY OF FIFTEEN, AND MY OLDEST AND DEAREST FRIEND, DICKIE HEATH, HAVING JUST STOLEN A CAR FROM THE PARKING LOT OF A SHOP EASY AND FINDING OURSELVES WITH NOTHING MUCH TO DO, ENTERED A HOUSE ON FOX HILL LANE. WHILE DICKIE RIFLED THROUGH THE UPSTAIRS FOR VALUABLES, I ENTERED THE SITTING ROOM, WHERE, WHILE POCKETING A GOLD-LEAF PEN AND A SILVER HUMIDOR, I CAME ACROSS THE BOOK THAT COM-

PLETELY AND IRREVOCABLY CHANGED MY LIFE. . . .

MONTHS LATER, AS I SAT IN THE JUVENILE DETEN-
TION HOME, REREADING THOSE POEMS THAT HAD
OPENED UP THE ARTIST IN ME, I WAS BLINDSIDED BY
THE RAGING FIST OF MY INCARCERATOR, WHO
INFORMED ME THAT WALT WHITMAN'S "HOMOEROT-
IC, UNNATURAL, PORNOGRAPHIC SENTIMENTS" WERE
UNACCEPTABLE AND WOULD NOT BE ALLOWED IN
AN INSTITUTION DEDICATED TO REFORMING THE ILL-
FORMED. THAT WHITMAN, THAT GREAT BEAR OF A
MAN, ENJOYED THE PLEASURES OF OTHER MEN CAME
AS A GREAT SURPRISE TO ME AND MADE ME RECON-
SIDER THE "QUEERS" THAT I HAD PREVIOUSLY KICKED
AROUND.

AS THE TALL SHIPS SAILED INTO HUDSON HARBOR
IN CELEBRATION OF OUR NATION'S BICENTENNIAL, I,
A HOOLIGAN OF FIFTEEN, LANDLOCKED IN JOPLIN,
MISSOURI, SAILED INWARD UNDER THE GENTLE
PRODDING BREEZE OF MY SPIRITUAL MENTOR, WALT
WHITMAN. OUR COURSE WAS STEADY, OUR DESTINA-
TION CLEAR: I WOULD NO LONGER STICK UP SHOP
EASYS, STEAL CARS, VIOLATE THE HOMES OF OTHERS. I
WOULD BECOME AN ARTIST.

A most unlikely role model, you might think, but in the
nonjudgmental universe that is Cicely, the citizenry relies on
Chris not only for music but for philosophical speculation, liter-
ary readings, and town gossip. And, courtesy of a mail-order
theology degree obtained from the back pages of *Rolling Stone*
magazine, Chris also can be counted on to officiate at wed-
dings, funerals, and most town meetings as well. Maurice, Ed,

Holling, Shelly—even self-reliant Maggie and self-absorbed Joel—sooner or later, they all come by the radio station or over to Chris's trailer for advice.

As usual, it's crusty, seventy-five-year-old Ruth-Anne, proprietor of Cicely's general store, who puts her finger on just why. "Well, Chris does venture farther out there than most of us," she allows in "Burning Down the House," the episode in

which Chris the Artist builds a giant catapult, "but he usually brings back something very interesting."

And then he talks about it, filling the Alaskan airwaves with a veritable aurora borealis of streaming consciousness, insight, and observation. What follows is some of what he has to say on love, life, and just about any other subject you can think of, including himself.

PART I

RAPS, RANTS, AND WRENCHING TIMES

🦌 1 🦌
THE CHRIS STEVENS STORY

Whether it's the day's special at The Brick, Cicely's favorite restaurant, or a misty-voiced confession on KBHR's "Mea Culpa" show (in which callers unburden themselves of their guilty secrets), things tend to remind Chris of his own saga, particularly of growing up delinquently juvenile in Wheeling, West Virginia. (Incidentally, the names of some of those colorful characters that Chris is fond of recollecting—such as Uncle Roy, Chuck Vincent, and Earl P. Duffy—belong to actual folks that actor John Corbett grew up with.)

A CLEAR FORTY-EIGHT DEGREES IN CICELY, ALASKA, NORTH AMERICAN CONTINENT, PLANET EARTH. THIS IS CHRIS-IN-THE-MORNING ON KBHR. IT'S CRISP, CLEAN, LATE-AUTUMN MORNINGS SUCH AS THIS

THAT TAKE ME BACK TO THE WHEELING, WEST VIR-
GINIA, OF MY CHILDHOOD—MORNINGS WHEN MY
DAD WOULD TURN TO MY UNCLE ROY AND SAY, "PUT
THE BOY IN THE TRUCK, ROY, WE'RE GOING HUNT-
ING." I'D LAY BACK THERE WITH THE SKY SLIPPING BY
OVERHEAD, WHILE IN THE CAB DAD AND ROY PASSED
THE WHITE LIGHTNING BETWEEN THEM. . . .

SO, PEOPLE, TIME FOR MY ANNUAL HUNT WITH
HOLLING VINCOEUR ON THESE, THE LAST FEW DAYS
OF HUNTING SEASON—HOLLING WITH HIS SINGLE-
LENS REFLEX, ME WITH MY WINCHESTER. TIME TO
HEAD INTO THE FOREST PRIMEVAL AND SHOOT US
SOME FAIR GAME. SPEAKING OF WHICH, HERE COMES

MAGGIE O'CONNELL DOWN MAIN STREET WITH WHAT APPEARS TO BE A NICE-LOOKING TEN-POINT BUCK ACROSS HER HOOD.

Cars, visions, fair game—all big parts of the Chris Stevens story. There's also breaking and entering:

IT WAS A LONG-AGO WINTER'S DAY WHEN ME AND MY SOULFUL FRIEND RONNIE BARAD LIBERATED SEVERAL ALBUMS FROM SAM BLADE RECORDS IN DOWNTOWN WHEELING, WEST VIRGINIA. BACK AT RONNIE'S SAFE AND DRY, WE LISTENED ALL DAY TO OUR STOLEN STASH, BLUES MUSIC THAT GAVE SOUND AND NAME TO THAT BROODING SENSE OF TORMENT AND DESPAIR WE FELT SO STRONGLY AT NINETEEN AND STILL FEEL SOMETIMES TODAY, ESPECIALLY IN DEEP WINTER DAYS LIKE THIS.

WE DEDICATE THIS MUSIC TO YOU, RONNIE, JUST STARTING YOUR LATEST THREE-TO-FIVE IN LOMPOC, BECAUSE THE BEST WAY OUT OF WINTER IS THROUGH IT. LIKE CARL JUNG SAYS, EMBRACE YOUR GRIEF, FOR THERE YOUR SOUL WILL GROW.

YOU'RE TUNED TO K-BEAR IN CICELY, ALASKA. THIS IS CHRIS-IN-THE-MORNING AND TODAY WE HAVE THE BLUES.

WHEN I WAS SIXTEEN, DICKIE HEATH AND I STOLE A CAR AND DROVE IT ALL THE WAY TO BOCA RATON, FLORIDA. A CONVERTIBLE. BIG SILVER PONTI-AC. WE DROVE STRAIGHT THROUGH, ALL NIGHT, TOP

DOWN, RADIO BLASTING. I REMEMBER LOOKING UP AT A SKY FULL OF STARS AND THINKING, THIS IS IT— THIS IS AS GOOD AS IT GETS. AND IT WAS. UNTIL LAST NIGHT. . . . WOW.

Wow, indeed. Chris does have a tendency to take images, ideas, and convictions to the limit—and never more so than in "The Big Kiss" episode, when he was convinced that he had to make love to Maggie O'Connell, the most beautiful

woman in town, to "capture her spirit" and get his voice back. How did he know that he had to do it? A two-hundred-and-fifty-six-year-old Indian spirit told him, that's how.

There may be just a touch of exaggeration in his description of growing up a Stevens, too.

LIFE AT THE OLD STEVENS HUMBLE ABODE WAS LIKE THE FLIP SIDE OF NORMAN ROCKWELL, IF YOU KNOW WHAT I MEAN. MY DAD, HE WAS NEVER AROUND AND MOM HAD THIS HEAVY THING GOING WITH THAT TWIST-OFF-CAP WINE THAT KEPT HER FLAT ON THE COUCH MOST OF THE TIME. WHEN SHE DID GET UP, IT WAS USUALLY TO SEND ME OUT FOR A PACK OF SMOKES.

When Shelly Tambo innocently inquires about the Stevens family Thanksgiving, Chris nonchalantly replies:

MOM WOULD SWITCH OVER TO ASTI SPUMANTI. THAT WAS ABOUT IT. MY DOG, BUDDY, AND ME, WE'D SNEAK OUT, GO THROUGH THE NEIGHBOR'S TRASH. THERE WERE USUALLY SOME PRETTY GOOD SCRAPS. STUFFING, SOMETIMES. NEVER GOT A WISH-BONE . . .

Dickensian, at the very least. As for his old man, the Stevens père was "a bum—totally irresponsible. Every dollar he ever made he blew on slow horses, fast women, and cheap whiskey."

He was also a bigamist, which Chris finds out when he meets his black half brother, Bernard. But the father that Bernard remembers, although physically the same man, was a completely different being—dependable, solid, an upstanding pillar of his community. Although they were the same guy,

Bernard's pop was a wonderful father, while Chris's dad was just one of a long line of petty-criminal Stevens men.

WE QUIT EVERYTHING—SCHOOL, WORK, YOU NAME IT. THE ONLY THING WE NEVER QUIT IS DRINKING. OH, YEAH—AND TOBACCO.

And raising hell. Chris's mother, Rachel, "ran away with an itinerant forklift operator when Chris was thirteen," his lawyer, Mike the Bubble Man, tells the court at Chris's extradition hearing. "Suffice it to say, young Chris did not grow up with a healthy respect for authority."

Keeping up with that Stevens family outlaw tradition cost young Chris a year of his life. He recalls he was twenty-two . . .

I WOKE UP ONE DAY, I WAS TWENTY-THREE. LOST A WHOLE YEAR—THREE HUNDRED SIXTY-FIVE DAYS DOWN THE DRAIN.

I'VE BEEN ABLE TO PIECE TOGETHER SOME FRAGMENTS OF MY LOST YEAR FROM THE RECOLLECTIONS OF FRIENDS AND KIND STRANGERS. I'D JUST GOT OUT OF THE JOINT. I WAS TRYING TO PUT SOMETHING TOGETHER, WORKING IN THE STEEL MILL BACK HOME. THEN DAD DIED, AND THEN MY UNCLE ROY—FORTY-TWO AND FORTY-THREE RESPECTIVELY—AND THEN MY BACK WENT OUT. NEEDLESS TO SAY, I FREAKED. I'VE BEEN TOLD I SPENT SOME TIME WITH A "HOSTESS" IN MACON, GEORGIA. LIVED FOR A COUPLE OF MONTHS NAKED IN A CAVE IN THE JEMEZ MOUN-

TAINS IN NEW MEXICO. NO ONE AROUND, SO WHY NOT?

THERE WAS THIS NATURAL HOT SPRING WITH WATERCRESS GROWING AROUND IT. I GOT DOWN ON ALL FOURS AND GRAZED. YOU THINK SLOWER WHEN YOU GRAZE. . . .

"IN THE MIDDLE OF THE JOURNEY OF LIFE, I CAME TO MYSELF WITHIN A DARK WOOD WHERE THE STRAIGHT WAY WAS LOST. AH, HOW HARD IT IS TO TELL OF THAT WOOD, SAVAGE AND HARSH AND DENSE, THE THOUGHT OF WHICH RENEWS MY FEAR. SO BITTER IS IT THAT DEATH IS HARDLY MORE." THAT'S DANTE, FOLKS, WRITING OF HIS OWN MIDLIFE CRISIS. THAT WAS THE FOURTEENTH CENTURY—SIX HUNDRED YEARS HAVE PASSED AND WE'RE STILL GOING THROUGH IT.

IT'S AT THAT MIDPOINT IN OUR PERSONAL CON-TINUUM WHEN OUR LIVES HANG IN DELICATE BAL-ANCE AND WE LOOK BEHIND TO SEE HOW FAR WE'VE COME AND REALIZE THAT OUR PAST IS NO LONGER A SOLITARY TRAIL THROUGH SECRET WOODS BUT A VISTA AS BIG AND EXPANSIVE AS THE OCEAN ITSELF, STRETCHING TO THE HORIZONS WITH OUR EXPERI-ENCES, NOTHING MORE THAN TINY, DOTLIKE SAIL-BOATS SWALLOWED UP BY THE ENORMOUS SEA. "NEL MEZZO DEL CAMMIN DI NOSTRA VITA MI RETROVAI PER UNA SELVA OSCURA CHE LA DIRRITTA VIA ERA SMARRITA." A TOAST FOR AULD LANG SYNE, TO MY OWN MIDLIFE CRISIS AT TWENTY-TWO, MY LOST

YEAR. TO EXCESS, FORGETFULNESS, FAILURE AND
BLINDNESS. IN MANY WAYS, MY FRIENDS, IT WAS THE
BEST FRIGGIN' YEAR OF MY LIFE.

As for his stretch in prison, this is how he remembers it.
It's a memory triggered by finding a can of green beans on a
shelf in Ruth-Anne's store:

FOUR HUNDRED GUYS, ALL EATING IN ONE BIG
ROOM. THE CLINK OF INDUSTRIAL SILVERWARE AND
TWO-PERCENT MILK IN TIN CUPS. GETTING ON INTO
THE WINTER MONTHS, THE SUN WAS ALWAYS DOWN
BY SUPPER TIME, SO WE ATE BY THE SODIUM LIGHTS
OVERHEAD—THOSE BIG OLD ORANGE SODIUM
LIGHTS. . . .
PRISON, RUTH-ANNE. I'M TALKING ABOUT WHEN I
WAS IN PRISON. THESE WERE THE BEANS! EVERY TUES-
DAY, EVERY THURSDAY, THESE BABIES HAD A PLACE
IN THE CORNER TRIANGLE OF MY DINNER TRAY.
THAT'S WHAT I'VE BEEN MISSING. I'VE BEEN MISSING
THE JOINT!

It was in jail where he spent the best Thanksgiving of his
life, Chris later tells his radio listeners:

I GOT A MESSAGE TODAY, FOLKS, VIA SOME TIN
CANS. AND DIG THIS: THERE WASN'T EVEN ANY
STRING HOOKING 'EM TOGETHER. THEY HELPED ME

RECALL THAT IT WAS BEHIND BARS, AMIDST FOUR HUNDRED CONS, THAT I ENJOYED THE BEST THANKS-GIVING OF MY LIFE.

ME AND THE OTHER GUYS FILED IN FROM THE YARD—THOSE OF US WHO WEREN'T IN SOLITARY—AND LINED UP IN THE DINING HALL. GOING THROUGH THE CHOW LINE, WE GOT TO TAKE AS BIG A HELPING AS WE WANTED—I GUESS EVEN IN THE CALABOZO WARDEN VIGLIETTA RECOGNIZED THE NEED TO OVERINDULGE ON THAT DAY OF ALL DAYS. PLASTIC PLATES BRIMMING WITH PRESSED TURKEY AND SWEET POTATOES AND GREEN BEANS . . .

AND, AFTER A BRIEF INTERRUPTION WHEN ONE OF THE NEW GUYS TRIED TO LIFT A CLEAVER FROM THE KITCHEN, JOY KING GEORGE GOT UP ON A CHAIR AND QUOTED A PASSAGE FROM PILGRIM'S PROGRESS. AND THEN, MAN, WE JUST ALL DUG IN.

JOY KING'S PUNK, JUNIOR THE WEATHERMAN, BROKE OUT A JUG OF APPLEJACK HE'D BEEN FERMENT-ING SINCE THE FOURTH OF JULY, AND WE PASSED THAT UNDER THE TABLE, SPIKING OUR CIDER WHEN WE WERE FREE OF WATCHING EYES. AND I REMEMBER THAT DOUG HANSON ACTUALLY GOT A LITTLE WACKED ON THE STUFF—STABBED SOME GUY JUST FOR PINCHING HIS YAMS. AND LITTLE BILLY BODNER TRIED TO GET A ROUND OF CHRISTMAS CAROLS GOING, EVEN THOUGH IT WAS A MONTH EARLY.

THE MELLOW SWEETNESS OF PUMPKIN PIE OFF OF A PRISON SPOON IS SOMETHING YOU WILL NEVER FORGET.

For Chris, prison was a road stop on a pilgrim's journey. As he muses after failing to teach Marilyn Whirlwind how to drive:

BEEN THINKING ABOUT WHERE I'D BE WITHOUT THOSE TEACHERS THAT TAUGHT ME. SERGEANT DUKE BECKER IN JUVVY BACK HOME. SARGE SHOWED ME AROUND THE LATHE, AND IN THE GYM THE UPPER-CUT FOLLOWED BY THE LEFT HOOK. POW! UNCLE ROY BOWER—RESPECT FOR THE RIFLE, THE RULES OF THE WOODS. ERASMUS—REASON, THE HARMONIOUS SHAPING OF MY MENTAL WORLD.

THEN IT WAS MY TURN. GRADUATION. FROM STUDENT, I BECAME TEACHER. A CHANCE TO GIVE BACK WHAT HAD BEEN GIVEN TO ME, TO LIGHT SOMEBODY ELSE'S FIRE. SO WHAT DID I DO? I BLEW IT,

PLAIN AND SIMPLE. FLAMED OUT. FLUNKED THE
COURSE. MY STUDENT CAME TO ME WITH A DESIRE
TO KNOW THE TIME. I TOLD HER HOW TO MAKE A
WATCH.

LIVE AND LEARN. POWER TO THE HOUR. ANOTHER
BROADCAST DAY ON K-BEAR.

As he often tells his listeners, prison was the place where
Chris Stevens educated himself.

WHEELING, WEST VIRGINIA, 1983. I'M IN THE JOINT.
PRISON LIBRARY, WORKING MY WAY BACKWARD
FROM Z. STENDHAL, PROUST . . . I'M IN THE LS.

AND EUREKA, BABY! JACK LONDON. MY MAIN
MAN.

IF WHITMAN GAVE ME POETRY, THEN MR.
LONDON TOOK ME TO A PLACE INSIDE ME I DIDN'T
KNOW EXISTED BUT RECOGNIZED INSTANTLY, LIKE I'D
BEEN HEADING THERE ALL MY LOST LIFE.

THERE WAS BUCK, BIG CIVILIZED MUTT FROM THE
SOUTH LAND, SLAPPED DOWN IN THE FRIGID NORTH
TO REDEFINE HIMSELF FOR WHAT HE REALLY WAS.

I WAS BUCK. BUCK WAS I. BUCK IS US.

The great teachers: Whitman, London, and a second-story
guy Chris met in stir, named Chuck.

CHUCK SPENT A MONTH IN THE INFIRMARY AFTER
BEING STABBED IN THE LUNG. WHEN HE CAME BACK
TO THE PRISON LAUNDRY WHERE WE BOTH WORKED,

CHUCK SAID TO ME, "CHRIS, LIVE EVERY DAY LIKE IT MIGHT BE YOUR LAST."

SURE, THAT'S A TIRED OLD CHESTNUT, I KNOW. BUT TRY ROASTING IT LIKE THIS: IT OUGHTA BE SPRING EVERY DAY; EVERY DAY WE OUGHTA WAKE UP BRAND NEW.

On yet another broadcast day—Thanksgiving, to be exact—Chris's nostalgia for the good old days leads him to make an on-air phone call to the guys still hanging out in the West Virginia State Penitentiary:

ON THIS OFFICIAL TURKEY DAY, LADIES AND BIRDS, WE HAVE FOR YOU ANOTHER GROUNDBREAKING EVENT—THE FIRST EVER ON-THE-AIR TELEPHONE TIE-

IN TO THE LOWER FORTY-EIGHT. HOLD ON WHILE I LINK UP WITH MY HOME AWAY FROM HOME, THE STATE PEN NESTLED ALONG THE OHIO RIVER AMIDST THE WOODED HILLS OF WEST VIRGINIA.

> HELLO? WARDEN VIGLIETTA?
> Warden: YES, IT IS, CHRIS.
> WHOA! WE HAVE CONTACT! HAPPY T-DAY WARDEN!
> Warden: THANKS, CHRIS. YOU KEEPING YOUR NOSE CLEAN, I TRUST.
> YES SIR, WARDEN, I AM.
> Warden: GOOD TO HEAR IT. NOW, I JUST WANT TO MAKE IT CLEAR: IF I HEAR INAPPROPRIATE LANGUAGE OF ANY KIND COMING OVER THIS LINE, I'M PULLING THE PLUG IMMEDIATELY—NO IFS, ANDS, OR BUTS. UNDERSTAND?
> YOU GOT IT, WARDEN VIGLIETTA.
> Warden: ALL RIGHT.

Chris can hear the clang of a steel door and then his prison buddies Rhodes and Billie are on the line. Chris is thrilled.

Back in the pen, things remain unchanged. Yancy's been denied parole . . .

SAME OLD YANCY, HUH?

Lonnie Pearl's doing two weeks in solitary . . .

NO KIDDING? LONNIE THE LAMB?

Billie: HE GOT CAUGHT WITH A SHIV UNDER HIS
MATTRESS. SOME LAMB, EH?
WHAT ABOUT JOY KING?
Rhodes: GEORGE? HE'S OUT OF HERE—FINALLY
WENT STATE'S EVIDENCE.

WISE MOVE. I'VE BEEN THINKING ABOUT YOU GUYS
A LOT, AND . . . GOD, I CAN'T TELL YOU HOW GREAT IT
IS TO HEAR YOUR VOICES AGAIN.

On yet another holiday, Chris recalls another unique voice
that helped to further expand his growing consciousness. He
begins by reminding his listeners of an old legend—that on
Christmas Eve, at midnight, all the animals fall on their knees
and speak, praising the newborn Jesus:

BACK IN THE WINTER OF '68, MY DAD WAS DOING
A SHORT TERM FOR D AND D. MOM WAS—I'M NOT
SURE WHERE MOM WAS.
ANYWAY, I WAS HOME ALONE CHRISTMAS EVE
AND I STAYED UP LATE TO SEE IF MY DOG, BUSTER,
WOULD TALK. HE DID.
AT LEAST I THINK HE DID. I DON'T REMEMBER
BUSTER'S EXACT WORDS, BUT THAT'S NOT IMPOR-
TANT. WHAT MATTERS IS THAT A SEVEN-YEAR-OLD
BOY EXPERIENCED HIS OWN PERSONAL EPIPHANY.
MY POINT? IT'S THAT CHRISTMAS REVEALS ITSELF TO
EACH OF US IN A PERSONAL WAY—BE IT SECULAR OR
SACRED. WHATEVER CHRISTMAS IS—AND IT'S MANY
THINGS TO MANY PEOPLE—WE ALL OWN A PIECE OF

IT. KINDA LIKE SANTA'S BAG—INSIDE THERE'S A GIFT FOR EVERYONE.

MY CHRISTMAS WISH FOR YOU TONIGHT: MAY YOUR DOG TALK.

Which, in Cicely, is not a particularly outrageous prospect. After all, in these mystical Alaskan woods dead lovers reincarnate as flirtatious malamutes, trees wail, and Indian spirits inhabiting grizzly bears take human form to pay court to Mary Margaret O'Connell.

Cicelians, then, can be expected to take it in stride when Chris announces one day that he's adopting a new heritage:

JAMBO, CICELY. THIS IS CHRIS-IN-THE-MORNING COMIN' AT YOU ONE LAST TIME. IT IS WITH A HEAVY BUT HUNGRY HEART THAT I BID YOU ALL FAREWELL, AS NEEDS I MUST RESPOND TO THE MYSTERIOUS WAYS OF HEART AND MIND. MY BROTHER'S ARRIVAL HAS BEEN AN EPIPHANY FOR YOUR LOCAL DEEJAY, A KARMIC TRIP WIRE IGNITING A DEEPER AWARENESS OF MY CONNECTIONS TO THE PLANET. MY BROTHER ALSO BROUGHT WITH HIM THE FINANCIAL MEANS FOR ME TO EXPLORE MY NEWFOUND IDENTITY. FOR THOSE OF YOU UNFAMILIAR WITH THE LATEST CHAPTER OF THE STEVENS SAGA, I'VE INHERITED HALF OF MY FATHER'S SIXTY-THOUSAND-DOLLAR BEQUEST TO HIS SONS.

SO THAT'S IT, FOLKS. MY HEART BEATS TO THE AFRICAN DRUM, MY BLOOD FLOWS WITH THE RIVER

NIGER. TODAY, MY FRIENDS, AND HENCEFORTH, I, CHRISTOPHER STEVENS, FORMALLY DECLARE MYSELF TO BE A PERSON OF COLOR. I'M OFF TO AFRICA, CICELY. <u>AVE ATQUE VALE</u>. HAIL AND FAREWELL.

But of course, Chris stays in Cicely and it's half brother Bernard who eventually makes the pilgrimage to Africa. Naturally, Chris muses on the air about the Larger Implications:

WHY THE SUDDEN TURN IN EVENTS? AS STEPHEN SONDHEIM WROTE IN <u>SUNDAY IN THE PARK</u>, "WE CHOOSE THINGS. AND THEN WE LOSE THINGS." YOU KNOW, OTHER THAN THIRTY THOUSAND DOLLARS, MY DADDY DIDN'T LEAVE ME MUCH IN LIFE, BUT THERE IS SOMETHING HE USED TO SAY:

"WATCH OUT FOR TOMORROW, SON, OR IT'LL KICK YOU IN THE HEAD." THANKS, DAD.

YOU'RE LISTENING TO CHRIS-IN-THE-MORNING ON K-BEAR, FIVE SEVENTY ON YOUR AM DIAL, THE VOICE OF THE BOROUGH OF ARROWHEAD COUNTY . . .

2
EXPLORE AND EVOLVE

While perhaps not exactly going where no man has gone before, Chris and his fellow Cicelians have gotten fairly far out there. Take the time Cicely awoke to K-BEAR'S . . .

. . . BELATED APOLOGY TO THE MUCH MALIGNED CHICKEN LITTLE. TURNS OUT YOU WERE RIGHT—THE SKY IS FALLING. THE NATIONAL SPACE ADMINISTRATION INFORMS US THAT UNCLE SAM'S COM-SAT 4 SATELLITE IS IN A RAPIDLY DECAYING ORBIT. THAT'S THEIR WAY OF SAYING A TON OF ANGRY SPACE TRASH IS HEADING BACK HOME AT FIFTEEN THOUSAND MILES AN HOUR.
WHAT DOES THAT MAKE ME THINK OF? MAKES ME THINK OF A TRICERATOPS, INNOCENTLY MUNCHING A PALM FROND WHEN OUT OF THE SKY, WHAMMO—

A METEOR SUCKER-PUNCHES OLD MOTHER EARTH. NEXT THING YOU KNOW, THAT TRICERATOPS, ALONG WITH A HUNDRED AND SEVENTY-FIVE MILLION YEARS OF DINOSAUR EVOLUTION, IS NOTHING BUT HISTORY.

TO THAT UNSUNG TRICERATOPS AND ALL ITS KIN, HERE'S A SONG FOR YOU. . . .

A meteor may have killed off the dinosaurs, but it was death by satellite that befell Rick, Maggie's latest hapless boyfriend. The impact, Chris is told, "fused man and machine."

WHEN I HEARD ABOUT RICK, THE FIRST THING I THOUGHT WAS, "KLAATU, BARADA, NIKTO," THOSE IMMORTAL WORDS THAT TOGGLED OFF THE ROBOT GORT IN THE DAY THE EARTH STOOD STILL. WHEN THAT MOVIE WAS MADE, ROBOTS WERE JUST THE STUFF OF FICTION. BUT, HEY, NOT ANY MORE. ARTIFICIAL INTELLIGENCE, ROBOTICS, BIO-IMPLANTS . . . NOT ONLY ARE WE MAKING SMART MACHINES, WE'RE BECOMING SMART MACHINES.

SO WHAT'S THAT GOT TO DO WITH RICK, YOU SAY? WELL, I'M THINKING HE MIGHT JUST BE THE NEXT STEP IN THIS EVOLUTIONARY PROCESS. YESTERDAY, WHEN THAT SWEET FLOWER OF NASA'S IMAGINATION MARRIED RICK, HE CROSSED THE LINE BETWEEN MAN AND MACHINE. HE BECAME THE FUTURE . . . HOMO NOVUS, THE NEW MAN. RICK, HERE'S ONE FOR YOU—"TELSTAR" BY THE ENGLISH TORNADOES.

Space satellites and the cosmos are very much on Chris's mind. The thought of the *Voyager* in interstellar space sets him to reciting from T. S. Eliot's "Four Quartets":

"WE SHALL NOT CEASE FROM EXPLORATION AND THE END OF ALL OUR EXPLORING WILL BE TO ARRIVE WHERE WE STARTED AND KNOW THE PLACE FOR THE FIRST TIME."

WHY THE T. S. ELIOT, YOU ASK? WELL, GOT A BULLE-TIN HERE FROM OUR FRIENDS AT JPl. SEEMS EARTH'S HAPPY PILGRIM, THE <u>VOYAGER 1</u> SPACECRAFT, NOW 7.2 BILLION KILOMETERS FROM HOME, IS PASSING THROUGH THE HELIOPAUSE, ZIPPING OUT OF OUR

SOLAR SYSTEM, AND INTO THE BOSOM OF THE MILKY WAY. GOOD LUCK AND GODSPEED TO YOU, OUR NOBLE EMISSARY. IT'S A TRIP WE EARTH-BOUND STARGAZERS WOULD ALL LOVE TO TAKE.

The *Voyager* even inspires Chris to do a little reading aloud from a children's book:

<u>PADDLE-TO-THE-SEA</u>, FOLKS—THE STORY OF AN INDIAN BOY WHO SENT A TOY CANOE ON A JOURNEY HE HIMSELF WAS TOO YOUNG TO TAKE.

WE DO THE SAME, YOU KNOW. <u>VOYAGER, PIONEER, GALILEO</u>—OUR STANDARD-BEARERS, IN THE ETERNAL HUMAN CRUSADE—EXPLORATION. AND NOW WE'VE HIT THE COSMIC TRAIL. WHY? OL' EARTH'S PLAYED OUT. LESS THAN A HUNDRED YEARS AGO, AMUNDSEN COULD BE THE FIRST HUMAN BEING TO REACH THE SOUTH POLE, AND FALCON SCOTT COULD DIE TRYING.

NOW? WELL, LAST YEAR CHINA HAD TO CLOSE MOUNT EVEREST. TOO MUCH LITTER. THE WORLD'S BECOME A FRAGILE PLACE—NOT TO BE CONQUERED BUT TO BE PROTECTED, CODDLED, NURSED LIKE A BABY.

SO WHAT DO WE DO? WE LAUNCH OUR SURRO-GATES INTO INTERSTELLAR SPACE, DREAMING OF THAT ONE FINE DAY WHEN WE OURSELVES CAN GO.

THERE ARE PROBABLY SOME FOLKS OUT THERE WHO'RE SAYING, "I'M NEVER GOING TO HAVE A RUSH LIKE THAT. EARTH'S A PARKING LOT AND OUTER SPACE IS JUST TOO PRICEY." WELL, LEMME TELL YOU, THERE ARE LOTS OF WAYS TO BLAZE A TRAIL. I OFTEN

WONDER ABOUT THOSE UNSUNG HEROES OF THE PAST—LIKE THE PREHISTORIC GOURMET WHO LOOKED AT A LOBSTER AND SAID, "I'M GONNA EAT THAT." OR THE FIRST HEALER WHO PICKED UP A KNIFE AND SAID. "LET'S OPERATE." SEE, ADVENTURES COME IN LOTS OF SHAPES AND SIZES—FROM GETTING A HAIRCUT TO FALLING IN LOVE. JUST PUTTING YOURSELF BEHIND THE WHEEL AND BACKING OUT OF THE DRIVEWAY—WELL, THAT CAN BE A SUBLIME ACT OF FAITH AS WELL AS A MONUMENTAL ACT OF COURAGE.

True curiosity always takes courage, Chris reminds the townsfolk.

THE BANE AND BLESSING OF HUMAN NATURE, THAT OL' CAT KILLER, CURIOSITY. SOMETHING SO DEEPLY IMBEDDED IN OUR PSYCHES, IT SCREAMS TO US FROM COUNTLESS MYTHS—PANDORA, EVE, LOT'S WIFE . . .

KNOWLEDGE DOESN'T COME CHEAP. THING IS— GOOD OR BAD, CURIOSITY IS WOVEN INTO OUR DNA LIKE TONSILS, LIKE THE OPPOSABLE THUMB. IT IS THE FIRE UNDER THE ASS OF HUMAN EXPERIENCE!

The human experience . . . curiosity means change, and change means evolution. And harmony, as Chris well knows, means being in touch with our carnivore/predator past.

NOT FOR NOTHING WERE WE GIVEN THESE INCISORS. THEY'RE FOR TEARING INTO MEAT—BLOOD

DRIPPING OFF THE FANGS. AND, YOU KNOW, IT'S GOOD TO KILL MEAT BEFORE YOU EAT IT. OTHERWISE, IT TENDS TO SCREAM. . . .

TAKE THE NASKAY INDIANS. THEY BELIEVE TO THIS DAY THE DESTRUCTION OF THEIR PEOPLE CAME FROM EATING DOMESTIC INSTEAD OF WILD ANIMALS. WE MAY BE FOUR HUNDRED GENERATIONS REMOVED FROM THE AFRICAN PLIOCENE, WHEN WE LEFT HOME IN THE MORNING WITH SPEARS IN OUR HANDS, BUT THERE'S NO BETTER ANTIDOTE FOR OUR CURRENT DOMESTICATION THAN TO STALK SOME WILD BEAST THROUGH THE TALL TIMBER. PLUS, BOTTOM LINE? IT'S A GAS.

WILD BIRD, CREATURE OF AIR AND FEATHER— TODAY IS A GOOD DAY TO DIE. IN DYING WE ARE TRYING, AND IN TRYING WE ARE BOTH FORGIVEN.

MAN BECOMES THE FOOD OF THE DIVINITY HE WORSHIPS.

THERE'S A DARK SIDE TO EACH AND EVERY HUMAN SOUL. WE WISH WE WERE OBI-WAN KANOBI, AND FOR THE MOST PART WE ARE, BUT THERE'S A LITTLE DARTH VADAR IN ALL OF US. THING IS, THIS AIN'T NO EITHER/OR PROPOSITION. WE'RE TALKING ABOUT DIALECTICS, THE GOOD AND THE BAD MERGING INTO—US. YOU CAN RUN BUT YOU CAN'T HIDE.

MY EXPERIENCE? FACE THE DARKNESS. STARE IT DOWN. OWN IT. AS BROTHER NIETZSCHE SAID, BEING HUMAN IS A COMPLICATED GIG. GIVE THAT OL' DARK NIGHT OF THE SOUL A HUG! HOWL THE ETERNAL YES!

Howling the eternal Yes is one thing. Petty theft is quite another. Or is it? When Ed catches Chris boosting "essentially useless" electric appliances, this is how Chris explains his actions:

WILDNESS, ED. WE'RE RUNNING OUT OF IT. EVEN UP HERE IN ALASKA. PEOPLE NEED TO BE REMINDED THAT THE WORLD IS UNSAFE AND UNPREDICTABLE. AND AT A MOMENT'S NOTICE, THEY COULD LOSE EVERYTHING. LIKE THAT.

I DO IT TO REMIND THEM THAT CHAOS IS ALWAYS OUT THERE, LURKING BEYOND THE HORIZON. THAT PLUS, SOMETIMES, ED, SOMETIMES YOU HAVE TO DO SOMETHING BAD—JUST TO KNOW YOU'RE ALIVE.

"THE WILD THINGS ROARED THEIR TERRIBLE ROARS AND GNASHED THEIR TERRIBLE TEETH AND ROLLED THEIR TERRIBLE EYES AND SHOWED THEIR TERRIBLE CLAWS, BUT MAX STEPPED INTO HIS PRIVATE BOAT AND WAVED GOOD-BYE AND SAILED BACK OVER A YEAR AND IN AND OUT OF WEEKS AND THROUGH A DAY AND INTO THE NIGHT OF HIS VERY OWN ROOM WHERE HE FOUND HIS SUPPER STILL WAITING FOR HIM AND IT WAS STILL HOT. . . ."

THANK YOU, MR. SENDAK, FOR REMINDING US THAT WE SHOULD NEVER LOSE TOUCH WITH THE WILD AND UNTAMABLE SPIRIT WITHIN US ALL. MAY-HEM HAS GOTTEN A BAD RAP AND CHAOS HAS TAKEN IT ON THE CHIN IN THESE PATHOLOGICALLY NORMAL AND RATIONAL TIMES. EVEN UP HERE IN ALASKA, WE'RE TURNING OUR BACK ON THE BEAST.

WE'VE OPTED FOR THE ZOO, WHERE THE LION CAN'T EAT YOU INSTEAD OF THE JUNGLE, WHERE HE CAN. <u>QUELLE DOMMAGE.</u> WHAT A DRAG.

But while Chris fancies himself an outdoorsman, he does understand the guilt that Joel feels the first time he shoots a bird.

THE SHAME OF CAIN SYNDROME. THE FIRST ONE ALWAYS SEEMS LIKE A BROTHER.

I DRAW THE LINE AT EATING FLIGHTLESS BIRDS . . . I FEEL TOO CLOSE TO BEING ONE MYSELF.

3
LIFE 'N' DEATH, LOVE 'N' PAIN, FATE AND THE PARALLEL UNIVERSE

When you're a philosopher, there's just no end to grappling with the Big Questions. Where do we come from? Where are we going? What does it mean to be human? Is it a random universe? Why is love so hard to find?

TELL YOU SOMETHING, FOLKS—RECENT EVENTS HAVE SET ME PONDERING THAT OLD ONTOLOGICAL RIDDLE: LIFE—IS IT RANDOM OR SYSTEMATIC?
LOVE DOESN'T EXIST IN A VACUUM. IT EXISTS IN A CONTEXT. ALWAYS. AND, SEE, I FELL IN LOVE WITH A WOMAN WHOSE DOG I RAN OVER. AND SHE FELL IN LOVE WITH ME, THE MAN WHO RAN OVER HER DOG. AND WHEN I LIED TO HER ABOUT THAT PARAKEET— YOU REALIZE WHAT I DID? I TOOK OUR LOVE OUT OF CONTEXT.

FIRST THE DOG, NOW THE BIRD. SHE'LL THINK I DID IT ON PURPOSE. AND MAYBE SHE'D BE RIGHT. I MEAN, WHO KNOWS WHAT KIND OF SUBCONSCIOUS FORCES ARE DRIVING ME?

From Holling's bar to Ruth-Anne's store to anywhere a radio dial is tuned to KBHR, Cicelians are contemplating the perennial issues.

WE ALL CARRY SO MUCH PAIN AROUND IN OUR HEARTS. LOVE AND PAIN AND BEAUTY—THEY SEEM TO GO TOGETHER, ONE TIDY, CONFUSING PACKAGE. IT'S A MESSY BUSINESS, LIFE. HARD TO FIGURE. FULL OF SURPRISES. SOME GOOD, SOME BAD. ANYWAY, MAGGIE, IF YOU'RE LISTENING OUT THERE,

THIS ONE'S FOR YOU . . .

Maggie isn't the only one spending more than the average amount of time struggling with the mysteries of life and love. They also keep Holling awake nights, worrying about things like the "seemliness" of his relationship with Shelly, his beautiful—and decades-younger—paramour. Naturally, it's to Chris that he goes for advice.

UNSEEMLY? NO, HOLLING, I DON'T SEE IT AS UNSEEMLY, OR UNBECOMING. NO. I MEAN, PERSON-ALLY, I DON'T BELIEVE IN CHRONOLOGICAL AGE. SHELLY COULD HAVE AN OLD SOUL AND YOU COULD HAVE A YOUNG ONE. IN FACT, SHE COULD EVEN BE OLDER THAN YOU.

TAKE A LOOK AT HISTORY. IT'S CRAWLING WITH MAY–DECEMBER ROMANCES. STROM THURMOND—GUY IS A U.S. SENATOR. SUPREME COURT JUSTICE WILLIAM O. DOUGLAS. CHARLIE CHAPLIN. FRED ASTAIRE. JERRY LEE LEWIS . . . JERRY LEE LEWIS. "GREAT BALLS OF FIRE"? HIS WIFE WAS THIRTEEN.

LOVE KNOWS NO BOUNDARIES, HOLLING. AGE, RACE, RELIGION, SEX—IT MOWS 'EM ALL DOWN.

When Shelly and Holling finally do decide to tie the knot, it's Chris who's elected to officiate. Of course, he expresses his joy at the news over the airwaves of KBHR.

ON OCCASIONS LIKE THESE, MY THOUGHTS TURN TO MARRIAGE. I THINK OF THE DALAI LAMA, THE POPE, AND MOTHER TERESA, VERY SPIRITUAL PEOPLE WHO NEVER TOOK THE PLUNGE; AND ON THE OTHER

HAND, YOU HAVE ELIZABETH TAYLOR AND MICKEY ROONEY, WHO COULDN'T GET ENOUGH OF A GOOD THING. WHAT CAN WE MAKE OF THIS DICHOTOMY, EXCEPT TO WISH OUR FRIENDS A LONG LIFE FILLED WITH FULLNESS.

Perhaps that speech had something to do with Holling's decision to back out of the wedding.

When Shelly needs to get unattached from her hockey player first husband, Wayne Jones of the Saskatoon Seals, naturally she does it the Cicely way: Dispense with the legal niceties and get Chris-in-the-Morning to handle the divorce proceedings over the air.

USED TO BE WHEN PEOPLE TOOK THE MARRIAGE VOW, "TIL DEATH DO US PART" MEANT JUST THAT. BUT AS OFTEN AS NOT THESE DAYS, PEOPLE TAKE A LOOK AT EACH OTHER AFTER A FEW YEARS IN THE MARITAL SACK AND SAY SEE YA LATER, JACK.

AND MAYBE THAT'S GOOD. WOLVES MATE FOR LIFE, BUT OUR SPECIES LIVES A LOT LONGER, MAYBE TOO LONG TO STAY HITCHED TO THE SAME POST. WELL, INDIVIDUAL OPINION ASIDE, DIVORCE LOOKS LIKE IT'S HERE TO STAY. SO INSTEAD OF SEEING IT AS A KIND OF FAILURE OR DEAD END, WHY NOT CELEBRATE DIVORCE AS THE BEGINNING OF SOMETHING? A FRESH START. ANOTHER CHANCE TO STEP UP TO THE BIG WHEEL. LIKE SWAMI BODHIDHARMA SAYS, YOU CAN'T HAVE A THING UNTIL YOU LET IT GO. IN OTHER WORDS, WHEN THINGS LOOK REAL BAD, MAYBE IT'S BETTER TO FIND A NEW WAY OF LOOKING AT THEM.

AND SO WE'RE HERE TO DO A DIFFERENT KIND OF CEREMONY TODAY—THE DIVORCE OF A COUPLE WHO PROBABLY GOT MARRIED TOO YOUNG, BEFORE THEY REALLY KNEW WHAT THEY WERE DOING, AND THEN REALIZED THEY'D MADE A TERRIBLE MISTAKE. WAYNE, YOU STILL THERE?

WE'VE GOT WAYNE JONES HERE ON THE LINE FROM SASKATOON, SASKATCHEWAN. WAYNE IS THE STARTING LEFT WING FOR THE SASKATOON SEALS. AND HERE IN THE STUDIO, HIS SOON-TO-BE-EX-WIFE, SHELLY TAMBO. . . .

OKAY. SHELLY. WAYNE. YOU GOT MARRIED A FEW

YEARS AGO AND IT DIDN'T WORK OUT. BUT THAT'S OKAY. YOU'VE GOT YOUR WHOLE LIFE IN FRONT OF YOU AND YOU'VE BOTH FOUND OTHER PEOPLE TO HOOK UP WITH. . . .

SO. HERE GOES. SHELLY TAMBO. DO YOU UN-TAKE WAYNE JONES AS YOUR LAWFULLY WEDDED HUS-BAND? AND DO YOU, WAYNE JONES, UN-TAKE SHELLY? WELL, THEN, BY THE POWER INVESTED IN ME TO MARRY, I NOW UNDO WHAT ANOTHER BROTHER OF THE CLOTH HAS DONE. NO PROBLEM.

To some, that attitude may seem casual or even cavalier, but it isn't. It's just nonjudgmental.

SOME THINGS ARE BETTER LEFT ALONE. CERTAIN THINGS WE'RE NOT MEANT TO TAMPER WITH OR TO POSSESS. AND THAT'S OKAY. BECAUSE HAPPINESS DOESN'T COME FROM <u>HAVING</u> THINGS—RIGHT? IT COMES FROM BEING <u>PART</u> OF THINGS.

Chris becomes very much a part of some peculiar things when he accidentally runs over a dog and then himself gets run over by love when he meets the late pooch's beautiful owner.

IT'S ONE THING TO ACCEPT THE CONCEPT OF RAN-DOM DEATH IN AN INDIFFERENT UNIVERSE, SURE, BUT TO BE THE <u>INSTRUMENT</u> OF THAT DEATH. . . . WHEW.

DOSTOYEVSKY ONCE DESCRIBED THE SENSATION HE'D EXPERIENCE JUST BEFORE HAVING A SEIZURE. IT WAS A FEELING OF IMPENDING REVELATION, AS IF HE

WAS ABOUT TO LEARN A GREAT TRUTH, AS IF THE UNIVERSE WAS POISED TO SPREAD ITS SECRETS BEFORE HIM. THEN <u>POW</u>—HE'D HIT THE MAT.

I REALIZE NOW WHAT DOSTOYEVSKY MEANT. STANDING IN AMY'S PRESENCE, I FELT THAT SAME ELATION, THAT SAME BREATHLESS ANTICIPATION. AND WHAT ABOUT THE COSMIC SIGNIFICANCE? I MEAN, I HAVE TO ASK MYSELF, WAS RUSTY A SACRIFICIAL LAMB, JUST A CHESS PIECE WHOSE ONLY PURPOSE WAS TO BRING US TOGETHER? OR IS THERE A DARKER, MORE OMINOUS MEANING HERE?

WAS HE THE FIRST SHOE TO DROP? KNOW WHAT I'M SAYING? A DOMINO IN A SERIES OF EVENTS, ALL

FATED TO LEAD TO OUR MUTUAL ANNIHILATION . . .
I DON'T KNOW. I MEAN, I DON'T KNOW IF THIS IS A
PATTERN. OR IF IT'S ALL RANDOM. IS THE FUTURE
CARVED IN STONE? OR DO WE CREATE OUR OWN
DESTINY? WHO KNOWS?

Chris is hip to just one thing, he tells the fair Amy: "I
don't want to lose you." But of course, he does.

THE MOLECULES SHIFT, THEN EVERYTHING GOES
BACK TO NORMAL, BUT EVERYTHING'S DIFFERENT.

NOW, ALL KINDS OF PEOPLE LOVE ALL KINDS OF
PEOPLE, AND MOST OF IT DOESN'T MAKE ANY SENSE
AT ALL. WHEN YOU GET RIGHT DOWN TO IT, <u>LOVE</u>
DOESN'T MAKE A WHOLE LOT OF SENSE. HALF THE
TIME YOU TRAMPLE ON SOMEONE'S HEART. OTHER
HALF THE TIME, <u>YOUR</u> HEART GETS THE FOOTPRINTS.

Maybe it's fate—or so it seems sometimes. For instance,
there's the time Maggie came to Chris wondering if she should
tell Joel, who's about to fly back to New York on vacation, that
she's dreamed that his plane will crash.

IF YOU DON'T AND HE GOES DOWN IN THAT
PLANE, YOU'RE GOING TO HAVE TO LIVE WITH IT FOR
THE REST OF YOUR LIFE. ON THE OTHER HAND,
WHAT IF YOU TELL HIM AND THE FLIGHT HE
CHANGES <u>TO</u> TURNS OUT TO BE THE ONE THAT

CRASHES? THIS FATE THING CAN BE PRETTY TRICKY.

WE MAY HAVE BEEN FATED TO HAVE THIS CON-
VERSATION AND DECIDE WHATEVER WE DECIDE.
COULD BE.

I MEAN, WE'RE ASSUMING YOU HAVE FREE WILL,
WHICH ISN'T REALLY THAT SAFE AN ASSUMPTION.

Fate is kind of a sensitive subject with Maggie O'Connell,
whose boyfriends keep meeting untimely ends. When the satellite tunnels in from space and takes out Rick, Chris deals with
the issue of O'Connell's "curse" at the funeral, but first he

has to explain to the assembled citizens the small delay in the proceedings.

RICK'S COFFIN NEEDED SOME CUSTOMIZING, BUT I DON'T MIND STARTING WITHOUT HIM. A FUNERAL'S REALLY MORE FOR THE SURVIVORS—IN THIS CASE MAGGIE, WHO'S BEEN A SURVIVOR MORE TIMES THAN SHE'D CARE TO COUNT.

A LOT OF YOU KNOW ABOUT RICK'S PREDECESSOR, DAVE, WHO FELL ASLEEP ON A GLACIER AND FROZE TO DEATH. BUT BEFORE DAVE, THERE WAS GLEN—HE AND HIS VOLVO TOOK A WRONG TURN AND ENDED UP ON A MISSILE TEST RANGE. THEN THERE WAS BRUCE, THE VICTIM OF A FREAK CROQUET ACCIDENT. AND BEFORE HIM, HARRY—HE DIED . . . UH . . . HOW WAS IT? THAT'S RIGHT—THE POTATO SALAD.

Y'KNOW, SOME PEOPLE COULD LOOK AT THIS STRING OF FIVE DEATHS AND SAY, "HEY, THIS IS WEIRD. SOMETHING'S GOIN' ON HERE." BUT I WANT TO SAY, MAGGIE, ON BEHALF OF US ALL: WE DON'T THINK IT'S YOUR FAULT. WE DON'T BELIEVE IN ANY CURSE. RIGHT EVERYBODY?

C'MON, YOU CAN DO BETTER THAN THAT.

Maggie may never be able to look at potato salad again, but to Chris death and destiny are constant subjects for on-air speculation. Like after playing Ludwig Van, or after reading a selection from *War and Peace*.

YOU'VE BEEN LISTENING TO THE ADAGIO FROM BEETHOVEN'S SEVENTH SYMPHONY. I THINK LUDWIG PRETTY MUCH SUMMED UP DEATH IN THIS ONE. HE'D JUST ABOUT LOST HIS HEARING WHEN HE WROTE IT, AND I'VE OFTEN WONDERED IF THAT DIDN'T HELP TUNE HIM IN TO THE FINAL SILENCE OF THE GREAT BEYOND.

APROPOS OF ALL THAT, WE HAVE A COUPLE SCHED- ULING CHANGES FOR THOSE LOOKING AFTER THE BODY OF THE UNKNOWN PERSON. DOREEN MAYFAIR IS NURSING A SICK MALAMUTE AND CAN'T MAKE HER SEVEN P.M. SHIFT TONIGHT. SHE'D LIKE TO TRADE FOR BOB TREVER'S NINE O'CLOCK. THAT OKAY WITH YOU, BOB? AND RUTH-ANNE, YOU WANTED ME TO REMIND YOU—YOU'RE UP AT SIX.

ON A HAPPIER NOTE, CONGRATULATIONS AND L'CHAIM TO HOLLING VINCOEUR, WHO'S GETTING CIRCUMCISED DAY AFTER TOMORROW BY OUR OWN DR. FLEISCHMAN. FOR THOSE OF YOU UNFAMILIAR WITH THE PRACTICE, CIRCUMCISION IS THE SURGICAL REMOVAL OF THE FORESKIN OF THE PENIS. IN JEWISH AND ISLAMIC TRADITION IT HEARKENS BACK TO GOD'S COVENANT WITH ABRAHAM. IT WAS SORTA HOW ABRAHAM SIGNED ON THE DOTTED LINE.

IF YOU'RE LISTENING, HOLLING, I DON'T KNOW IF YOU HAVE PLANS FOR THE DISPOSAL OF YOUR FORE- SKIN, BUT YOU MIGHT CONSIDER THE HASIDIC CUS- TOM OF BURYING IT UNDER A FRUIT TREE. YOU

KNOW, A LITTLE NOD TO LIFE'S CYCLIC NATURE. ANY-
WAY, HOLLING, I'M SPINNING THIS ONE FOR YOU . . .

"THE PLACE CHOSEN FOR THE DUEL WAS SOME
EIGHTY PACES FROM THE ROAD ON WHICH THEIR
SLEDGES HAD BEEN LEFT, IN A SMALL CLEARING IN
THE PINE WOOD, COVERED WITH SNOW THAT HAD
THAWED IN THE WARMER WEATHER OF THESE LAST
FEW DAYS." IF PIERRE HADN'T MARRIED, IF HELENE

HADN'T CHEATED, IF PIERRE HADN'T LOST HIS TEMPER—A LOT OF IFS IN THIS LIFE.

THE DUEL ITSELF AT OUR NEXT READING OF <u>WAR AND PEACE.</u> IRONIC THAT IN THE PARALLEL UNIVERSE WE CALL REALITY, WE HAVE OUR OWN DUEL SCRIPTED IN. KIND OF MAKES YOU WONDER WHO'S WRITING <u>THIS</u> BOOK.

🐃 4 🐃
DREAMS, MAGIC, AND THE PSYCHEDELIC LAND OF PHYSICS

In the episode entitled "Get Real," the circus comes to town (well, actually, the water pump on the Ludwig Wittgenstein Masquerade and Reality Company's bus goes out, and the troupe has to hang around Cicely while it's being repaired). As a result, we learn that Chris Stevens, ex-delinquent, is no slouch in the theoretical physics department.

It's to be expected that Chris, being an autodidact, is a little hazy on algebra, but you can bet he's got the Superstring Theory down cold.

THIS HAD BEEN BUGGIN' ME FOR A LONG TIME. I WAS DOING A LITTLE CURSORY READING IN SUPER-STRING ATOMIC THEORY. BUT I HAD A HARD TIME 'CAUSE MY MATH IS WEAK.

I CAN ADD, SUBTRACT, DIVIDE, AND MULTIPLY, BUT YOU LOSE ME AT FRACTIONS. ANYWAY, IT SEEMS AS YOU PEEL BACK THE ONION OF THE ATOM, AS YOU GET INTO SMALLER AND SMALLER PARTICLES, YOU FIND THAT THEY MIGHT NOT BE PARTICLES AT ALL. . . . SO, SUBATOMIC PARTICLES MIGHT REALLY JUST BE VIBRATING WAVES OF ENERGY.

THE ESSENTIAL BUILDING BLOCK OF EVERYTHING IS NOTHING.

Or, as the circus magician (a former physicist himself) tells Chris, what he always hated about the physics business is that "everything is illusion."

This gets Chris to thinking about magic. (Incidentally, the "one version of the Arthurian legend" that Chris mentions in the following passage is a reference to *The Once and Future King* by T. H. White.)

WHEN WE THINK OF A MAGICIAN, THE IMAGE THAT COMES TO MIND IS MERLIN—LONG WHITE BEARD, CONE-SHAPED HAT—YOU KNOW. WELL, IN ONE VERSION OF THE ARTHURIAN LEGEND, THIS ARCHETYPAL SORCERER RETIRES, CHECKS OUT OF THE CONJURING BUSINESS. HIS REASON? THE RATION-ALISTS ARE TAKING OVER. THE TIME FOR MAGIC IS COMING TO AN END.

WELL, OL' MERLIN SHOULD'VE STUCK AROUND, 'CAUSE THOSE SAME RATIONALISTS, TRYING TO PUT A ROPE AROUND REALITY, FOUND THEMSELVES IN THE PSYCHEDELIC LAND OF PHYSICS, A LAND OF QUARKS AND GLUONS AND NEUTRINOS, A PLACE THAT REFUSES

TO PLAY BY NEWTONIAN RULES, THAT REFUSES TO PLAY BY ANY RULES AT ALL—A PLACE MUCH BETTER SUITED TO THE MERLINS OF THE WORLD.

IF THERE'S NOTHING OF SUBSTANCE IN THE WORLD, IF THE GROUND WE WALK ON IS JUST A MIRAGE, IF REALITY ITSELF REALLY ISN'T, WHAT ARE WE LEFT WITH? ON WHAT DO WE HANG OUR HAT?

MAGIC—THE STUFF NOT RULED BY "RATIONAL" LAW.
NOW, THAT MIGHT NOT SEEM TOO COMFORTING.
BUT STAY WITH ME. WHAT'S THE HEIGHT OF THE
IRRATIONAL, THE ZIP CODE OF THE MYSTERIOUS?
EXACTLY.

"O MY LUVE'S LIKE A RED, RED ROSE,
THAT'S NEWLY SPRUNG IN JUNE;
O MY LUVE'S LIKE THE MELODIE
THAT'S SWEETLY PLAYED IN TUNE.

AS FAIR ART THOU, MY BONNIE LASS,
SO DEEP IN LUVE AM I;
AND I WILL LUVE THEE STILL, MY DEAR,
TILL ALL THE SEAS GANG DRY.

TILL A' THE SEAS GANG DRY, MY DEAR,
AND THE ROCKS MELT WI' THE SUN:
O I WILL LOVE THEE STILL, MY DEAR,
WHILE THE SANDS O' LIFE SHALL RUN.

AND FARE THEE WEEL, MY ONLY LUVE,
AND FARE THEE WEEL AWHILE!
AND I WILL COME AGAIN, MY LUVE,
THOUGH IT WERE TEN THOUSAND MILE."

The poetic sentiments are courtesy of Robert Burns,
another world-class romantic. Like literary-minded romantics
everywhere, Chris Stevens is a dreamer and a student of nocturnal visions—particularly when the endless Arctic moonlight is
making everybody in Cicely just a tad extralunatic.

Sometimes, Chris's dreams tell him to construct grand sculptures; sometimes, when his subconscious is cross-wired with his half brother Bernard's, they tell him to go to Africa.

WHENEVER THERE'S A NEW MOON LOOMING ON THE HORIZON, SOMEONE WILL INEVITABLY CALL TO ASK, "HEY CHRIS, WHAT ABOUT THAT SUCKER?" AND I'LL USUALLY SAY SOMETHING CORDIAL LIKE, "OH, YEAH, IT'S A MARVELOUS NIGHT FOR A MOONDANCE" OR "I WONDER WHAT OL' SUN MYUNG MOON IS DOING TONIGHT?" BUT KNOWING HOW WE'VE ALL BEEN TOSSING AND TURNING THESE PAST FEW NIGHTS FOR FEAR OF WHERE OUR DREAMS ARE TAKING US, I AM NOT GOING TO PRETEND THAT THE MAN IN <u>THAT</u> MOON HAS OUR BEST INTERESTS AT HEART. HE'S TOO MUCH OF A KIDDER.

IN THE MEANWHILE, UNTIL THE BIG FELLA PACKS HIS BAGS AND HITS THE ROAD, PUT AWAY YOUR SHARP UTENSILS AND STAY CLOSE TO YOUR LOVED ONES IF YOU'RE LUCKY ENOUGH TO HAVE ANY. SEE YA IN THE MORNING, FOLKS, OR IN THE MOON-LIGHT—WHICHEVER COMES FIRST.

DREAMS ARE POSTCARDS FROM OUR SUBCON-SCIOUS, INNER SELF TO OUTER SELF, RIGHT BRAIN TRYING TO CROSS THAT MOAT TO THE LEFT. TOO OFTEN THEY COME BACK UNREAD: "RETURN TO SENDER, ADDRESSEE UNKNOWN." AND THAT'S A SHAME BECAUSE IT'S A WHOLE OTHER WORLD OUT THERE—OR IN HERE—DEPENDING ON YOUR POINT OF VIEW.

INDEED, FOR ALL WE KNOW THIS VERY MOMENT COULD BE NOTHING MORE THAN VAPORS OF OUR OWN IMAGINATIONS. AS BERTRAND RUSSELL MUSED, "I DO NOT BELIEVE THAT I AM NOW DREAMING, BUT I CANNOT PROVE THAT I AM NOT." POINT BEING, THERE COULD BE MORE TO OUR NOCTURNAL JOUR-NEYS THAN COMMONLY ACCEPTED OR CONSIDERED.

THIS IS CHRIS-IN-THE-MORNING COMING TO YOU ON K-BEAR FROM CICELY, ALASKA, IN THE HEART OF THE BOROUGH OF ARROWHEAD. I HAD A REALLY WEIRD DREAM LAST NIGHT AND I WANT TO TELL YOU ABOUT IT—BUT FIRST, THE WEATHER AND LOCAL NEWS.

IT'S A BEAUTIFUL DAY IN THE FORTY-NINTH STATE. CRISP AND CLEAR. INVIGORATING. INTOXICATING.

DARK. THERE'S A BREAKFAST SPECIAL AT HOLLING'S CAFÉ TODAY. EGGS BENEDICT, STEAK TARTARE, AND REINDEER SAUSAGE. ALL FOR A MERE $3.95. THE TWENTY-FOURTH ANNUAL BINGO CHAMPIONSHIP WILL BE HELD AT JFK MEMORIAL HALL STARTING IN ABOUT FIVE MINUTES. SO HURRY ON DOWN AND WIN YOURSELF A WEEKEND IN FAIRBANKS.

OKAY, SO, THE DREAM. I WAS WORKING ON AN ASSEMBLY LINE WITH MY FIRST TRUE LOVE, LESLIE FERGUSON. LESLIE, LESLIE. WHAT A GIRL. I USED TO WALK HER TO SCHOOL EVERY DAY. SHE ALWAYS SMELLED OF WOOL AND SOME KIND OF SWEET PER-FUME. ANYWAY, THERE WE WERE, IN MY DREAM, ON THE ASSEMBLY LINE, MAKING MECHANICAL FROGS. THEY COULD JUMP AND SING AT THE SAME TIME.

THEY SAY DREAMS ARE THE WINDOWS OF THE SOUL. TAKE A PEEK AND YOU CAN SEE THE INNER WORKINGS, THE NUTS AND BOLTS. I DON'T UNDER-STAND THE ASSEMBLY LINE, I FIND THE FROGS A LITTLE CONFUSING, BUT LESLIE FERGUSON RINGS BRIGHT AND TRUE.

FIRST LOVE. WE'VE ALL GOT ONE SOMEWHERE. THIS ONE'S FOR YOU, LESLIE.

Most everyone has a first love, it's true. In the case of Chris, though, there were two.

WHAT IS THE NEED TO NAME BUT THE NEED TO CLAIM, TO BE ABLE TO CALL A THING, TO CONJURE IT, TO MAKE IT YOUR OWN?

ANGEL BAILEY. SIXTH GRADE. ROSE TATTOO ON HER ANKLE, GRAVITY SWITCHBLADE. HOW MANY TIMES DID I WRITE HER NAME ON THE MARGINS OF MY NOTEBOOK, OVER EVERY PAGE OF EVERY TEST? CHRIS LOVES ANGEL. ANGEL LOVES CHRIS. ANGEL, ANGEL, ANGEL. THEY DIDN'T HAVE GRAFFITI THEN, BUT IF THEY DID, I'D HAVE TAGGED EVERY BRIDGE AND BUS IN WHEELING, WEST VIRGINIA.

WHAT'S IN A NAME?
IN THE CASE OF ANGEL,
VOLUMES.

Names are symbols, and when it comes to symbols . . .

"GHASTLY, GRIM, AND ANCIENT RAVEN, WAN-DERING FROM THE NIGHTLY SHORE
TELL ME WHAT THY LORDLY NAME IS ON THE NIGHT'S PLUTONIAN SHORE!
QUOTH THE RAVEN, "NEVERMORE."

WELL, THAT'S HOW MR. POE SAW THE RAVEN. A LOT OF REFERENCES IN WESTERN LITERATURE DO TEND TOWARD THE NEGATIVE. LIKE WITH MOST THINGS IN LIFE, WHEN IT COMES TO TRANSCENDEN-TAL SYMBOLS, ONE MAN'S SAVIOR IS ANOTHER MAN'S PAIR OF LEAD BOOTS.

5

SLIPPERY TRUTH 'N' ELUSIVE REALITY

Hardly a day goes by when Chris Stevens isn't brooding over reality versus mere appearance.

LIKE EVERY HUMAN BEING, I'VE TRIED TO MAKE SENSE OF THINGS. I'M NOT SURE I SUCCEEDED. I'M NOT SURE ANYONE CAN.

ISAAC NEWTON THOUGHT THE UNIVERSE FUNC-TIONED LIKE CLOCKWORK, A WELL-OILED MACHINE. THAT'S A COMFORTING VISION—NEAT, ORDERLY, PRE-DICTABLE. UNFORTUNATELY, IT'S A VISION THAT'S PRETTY MUCH BEEN SHOT TO PIECES BY RELATIVITY, QUANTUM MECHANICS, AND ALL THE OTHER BUGA-BOOS OF TWENTIETH-CENTURY PHYSICS.

THE UNIVERSE IS WEIRD! WE BREAK OUR TEETH

DEVELOPING THEORIES, EQUATIONS, SYSTEMS. AND WHERE DOES IT ALL LEAVE US?

"A SYSTEM IS LIKE THE TAIL OF TRUTH, BUT TRUTH IS LIKE A LIZARD. IT LEAVES ITS TAIL IN YOUR FINGERS AND RUNS AWAY, KNOWING FULL WELL THAT IT WILL GROW A NEW ONE IN A TWINKLING."

Or so said Ivan Sergeyevich Turgenev, the famous Russian novelist. As Chris puts it:

SOMETIMES REALITY IS AN ELUSIVE THING.

KUROSAWA'S <u>RASHOMON</u>: THE FINAL WORD ON REALITY. NAMELY, THERE ISN'T ANY. NOT JUST ONE, ANYWAY.

EINSTEIN SAID GOD DOESN'T PLAY DICE WITH THE UNIVERSE, BUT I DON'T KNOW. MAYBE NOT AS A WHOLE, BUT I THINK HE GETS A PRETTY BIG KICK OUT OF MESSIN' IN PEOPLE'S BACKYARDS.

He's not the only one. Ex-astronaut and would-be real estate mogul Maurice Minnifield does the same thing. When the body of Pierre Le Moulin, an alleged aide to Napoleon, turns up in Cicely, Maurice is all for turning the town into a tourist mecca. Of course, Chris has a few words to say about the whole subject.

HISTORY IS POWERFUL STUFF. ONE DAY YOUR WORLD IS FINE. THE NEXT IT'S KNOCKED FOR A META-

PHYSICAL LOOP. WAS NAPOLEON AT WATERLOO?
WOULD IT CHANGE WHAT I HAD FOR BREAKFAST?

It's too easy to confuse truth with facts, Chris tells Joel.

IT'S THE TRUTH THAT CHANGES.
CUSTER. HERO OR VILLAIN? CIVILIZER OR AGENT OF
GENOCIDE? THE TRUTH SLIPS AND TURNS, BUT THE
FACTS REMAIN THE SAME.
LET'S DISTINGUISH PARADOX FROM CONTRA-
DICTION, JOEL. CAN SOMETHING BE MORE THAN ONE
THING AT THE SAME TIME? FATHER, SON, AND HOLY
GHOST?

BUT WE DIGRESS. I OFFER THE POET'S VISION OF AN
ANCIENT URN: TRUTH IS BEAUTY AND BEAUTY
TRUTH.

Of course, where some see beauty, others, like Maurice,
see only opportunity.

BUILD A HYATT, THEY WILL COME. I THINK WE ALL
AGREE ON THAT. BUT TONIGHT I'M TROUBLED.

IT'S NOT THE LEVELING OF A SLEEPY LITTLE TOWN
INTO A COMMERCIAL EYESORE THAT BOTHERS ME.
[IT'S] THE METAPHYSICAL IMPLICATIONS.

UNLEASHING PIERRE CHANGES HISTORY. THAT'S
SOME HEAVY-DUTY TRAMPLING ON THE KARMA OF
THE COLLECTIVE UNCONSCIOUS. ARE WE READY TO
ACCEPT RESPONSIBILITY FOR THAT? WELL, I'M NO
MILITARY BUFF, BUT THOUSANDS OF THE OLD
FRENCH GUARD DIED AT WATERLOO. THOUSANDS OF
BRITISH AND PRUSSIANS DIED STOPPING THEM. TAKE
NAPOLEON OUT OF THAT LOOP AND WHAT'S LEFT?
HAVEN'T WE STRIPPED THE MEANING FROM THOSE
DEATHS, MADE A MOCKERY OF THE BLOODSHED?

OUR LIVES ARE FRAGILE THINGS, BUILT ON CREAKY
FOUNDATIONS. CHIP AWAY AT THE EDIFICE OF HIS-
TORY AND WE WEAKEN ONE OF THE FEW SPIRITUAL
TIMBERS WE HAVE.

CONSIDER: DID GEORGE WASHINGTON REALLY
CHOP DOWN THAT CHERRY TREE? DID DAVY CROCKETT
KILL A BEAR WHEN HE WAS ONLY THREE? PRETTY
UNLIKELY. BUT IT'S NICE TO THINK SO, ISN'T IT? IT

MAKES OUR LIVES EASIER TO BEAR. REVEALING PIERRE'S SECRET MIGHT TRIGGER A MAELSTROM OF SELF-DOUBT, LEAVING UNTOLD PSYCHIC DEVAS-TATION IN ITS WAKE. A METAPHYSICAL TSUNAMI, IF YOU WILL.

Nothing sets off that metaphysical tsunami like love, as the denizens of Cicely prove time and again, and there's nothing more bracing than this type of conundrum to send Chris's blood pulsing. When he meets Amy, the lovely mathematician of the episode entitled "Nothing's Perfect," it's over her dissertation-in-progress—using a computer to take pi to billions of digits—that Chris rhapsodizes. (Incidentally, according to *Webster's*, pi is "a transcendental number having a value to eight decimal places of 3.14159265.")

THE DIAMETER/CIRCUMFERENCE THING?
DECIMALS SPOOLING ON AND ON FOREVER AND EVER. . . .
THE CIRCLE! THE CONTINUUM! THE MYSTERY OF THE INFINITE!
A MESSAGE FROM GOD.

But infinitely more traumatic than his relationship with Amy, whose pets he keeps inadvertently killing, is his first meeting with Simon, the silent monk, at the monastery where Chris has gone on retreat.

EVER SINCE I READ ST. AUGUSTINE IN THE JOINT, I'VE BEEN REALLY INTO THE PHILOSOPHICAL, RELI-

GIOUS THING. AND SO FOR ME TO MEET A GUY
WHO'S ACTUALLY "DEAD TO THE WORLD"—I MEAN,
WOW, I CAN'T BEGIN TO TELL YOU. . . .

THE VOW OF SILENCE. THAT'S THE MIND BLOWER.
SEE, TALKING IS WHAT I DO. I'M A DEEJAY. BUT MORE
THAN THAT, IT'S A REAL NEED WITH ME—A CRAVING.
I'M LIKE A WORD JUNKIE. I NEVER SHUT UP.
I TALK TO <u>MYSELF</u>.
I TALK IN
MY <u>SLEEP</u>.

THE IDEA OF VOLUNTARILY TURNING OFF THAT
TAP! I CAN'T IMAGINE IT. IT'D BE LIKE—I DON'T

KNOW—ALL THE RIVERS IN THE WORLD JUST SLAMMED TO A STOP! NO CHURNING, NO FLOWING, NO WHITE WATER. JUST STILLNESS, CRUSHING STILL-NESS. I DONT THINK I COULD STAND IT, LOCKED UP LIKE THAT IN MY OWN PSYCHE. I'D COLLAPSE INTO MYSELF. I'D IMPLODE.

THIS IS REALLY INCREDIBLE TALKING TO YOU. IT'S LIKE PRAYING. I'D GIVE ANYTHING FOR SOME KIND OF SIGNAL, SOME INDICATION I'M GETTING THROUGH. . . .

Chris may or may not be getting through to the silent monk, but Simon certainly is getting through to Chris, right into his erotic dreams, speaking directly and most disconcertingly to his subconscious:

OKAY. THE THING IS, I'VE BEEN HAVING EROTIC FANTASIES ABOUT ONE OF THE MONKS HERE.

I'VE ALWAYS FELT SEXUALLY SECURE—MORE THAN THAT—<u>COMMITTED.</u> BUT HAS IT ALL BEEN A LIE? IS THIS MY TRUE SELF? THE SELF I CAME HERE TO DIS-COVER, THIS SELF THAT SITS HERE, PHYSICALLY AND EMOTIONALLY CONSUMED BY BROTHER SIMON?

Eventually Chris tells silent Simon himself about his disturbing dreams.

I GRABBED YOU, I KISSED YOU. IT WAS SO REAL. I CAN STILL TASTE THE COLD, BITTER ALUMINUM OF YOUR MASK. YOUR HANDS, THEY WERE DRIPPING WITH HONEY. I LICKED YOUR FINGERS CLEAN. YOU

PEELED OFF MY ROBE. THE BEES SWARMED, THEY STUNG ME. BUT I DIDN'T CARE. I PULLED YOU DOWN—ONTO THE GRASS. OH, GOD, BROTHER SIMON!

I KNOW, I KNOW. BUT IT'S WORSE FOR ME. I NEVER THOUGHT I WAS ATTRACTED TO MEN. I THOUGHT I LOVED WOMEN!

I'M SORRY, BROTHER SIMON! I DIDN'T MEAN TO BURDEN YOU WITH THIS. IF YOU COULD JUST FIND IT IN YOUR HEART TO FORGIVE ME.

GOD, I WANT TO SEE YOU WITHOUT YOUR CLOTHES ON. WHAT ARE YOUR LEGS LIKE? THEY'RE LONG, AREN'T THEY? STRONG . . .

NO, NO! FORGET I SAID THAT, BROTHER SIMON!

Chris may be conflicted and confused, but "Brother" Simon is not. "He" turns out to be a *she*—secretly living the contemplative life—and, as fate would have it, her real name is Chris.

It's not the first time the "gay thing" has become a factor in Cicely life. After all, the town was founded by Cicely and Roslyn, two independent-minded, turn-of-the-century lesbians, and it's currently home to an attractive and entrepreneurial male couple. This disturbs the hyper-macho Maurice so much that he decides to hand over his prized collection of show tunes and fondue dishes to the diplomatic Chris.

THEY THOUGHT YOU WERE GAY? THEN YOU'D BETTER HOLD ON TO THIS STUFF. THE THING IS, YOU DON'T WANT TO APPEAR TO BE OVERREACTING. YOU

WANT TO PRESENT AN IMAGE OF A MAN WHO'S COMFORTABLE WITH HIS SEXUALITY.

IT'S A CLICHÉ, MAURICE, BUT MEN WHO ARE FREAKED BY HOMOSEXUALS, WELL . . . THEY USUALLY HAVE SOME TENDENCIES IN THAT DIRECTION THEMSELVES.

But Maurice needs more convincing.

STILL HUNG UP ON THAT GAY THING, HUH?

IF YOU THINK ABOUT IT, YOU AND GAY MEN SHARE A LOT OF COMMON VALUES.

I WAS THINKING OF MILITARY TRADITION—DISCI-

PLINE, HONOR, LOYALTY—THAT KIND OF THING.
TAKE THE JANISSARIES, THE ELITE TROOPS OF THE
OTTOMAN EMPIRE. FOR A COUPLE HUNDRED YEARS,
THEY WERE THE MOST GUNG-HO, BLOODTHIRSTY
ARMY IN THE WORLD. THEY SLAUGHTERED MILLIONS,
LEVELED COUNTLESS CITIES. PILLAGED, TORTURED,
YOU NAME IT.

IT'S A WELL-KNOWN FACT: THEY PREFERRED THE
COMPANY OF MEN.

6
"IT'S NOT THE THING YOU FLING, IT'S THE FLING ITSELF": WOMEN, SEX, AND ART

There's nothing like some time off in the company of celibate men to remind a sensitive guy like Chris of the higher joys in life. We're talking women here—we're talking sex and art.

HEY, FOLKS, I'VE JUST COME BACK FROM A SHORT CRUISE ON THE RIVER OF SPIRITUAL RENEWAL. YOU MIGHT BE WONDERING: WERE MY GOALS MET? DID I HAVE THAT TRANSCENDENT MOMENT—THE EPIPHANY? YOU BET I DID.

YOU KNOW, WE MEN ARE ALWAYS BOOKING OUT. WE JOIN ARMIES, BASEBALL TEAMS, FRAT HOUSES—IN MY CASE, A MONASTERY—ALL TO THE EXCLUSION OF OUR FAIR SISTERS. BUT LET ME TELL YOU: IN THAT SEGREGATED, CELIBATE WORLD OF MEN, A DIVINE

HAND REACHED DOWN, GRABBED ME BY THE BELT STRAP AND GAVE A HARD YANK.

TO WHOM DID THIS AWESOME HAND BELONG? WOMAN.

YES, CICELY, MY METAPHYSICAL MOMENT—MY REVELATION—WAS THIS: FOR ME, THERE CAN BE NO SPIRITUALITY, NO SANCTITY, NO TRUTH . . . WITHOUT THE FEMALE SEX.

Words work well with women, as is demonstrated when Ed's freckle-faced paramour wants him to keep writing her sensual letters. Those love notes may be signed by Ed, but of course the true wordsmith behind the letters is Chris.

WHAT DO YOU WANT? <u>WORDS?</u> YOU LIKE THE WORDS . . .

WRITERS HAVE BEEN DOING IT FOR YEARS, EROTICIZING THE LANDSCAPE. FROM THE KAMA SUTRA TO HENRY MILLER. A FRENCH POET NAMED BAUDELAIRE DID A LOT OF INTERESTING STUFF WITH WET CAT FUR.

I'M GONNA WRITE YOU ONE MORE LETTER, BUT THEN YOU HAVE TO GO.

I'M GOING TO COMPARE YOU TO A SUMMER'S DAY.

When it comes to his art, Chris prizes originality right up there with Zenlike purity. Take the episode entitled "Burning Down the House," in which Chris decides to construct a trebuchet in order to catapult a cow.

LATEST REPORT FROM THE ART FRONT: PICKED UP TWO PETERBILT TRUCK SPRINGS FROM THE DUMP THIS MORNING. BEAUTIES. THEY'LL TAKE ABOUT A TON OF PRESSURE APIECE. I STILL NEED A HAND WINCH. ALSO, A BUTTERFLY BIT AND USE OF A DRILL PRESS.

ALONG THOSE LINES, I'D LIKE TO THANK THE FOLKS OVER AT PANIMSET DAIRY FARM FOR THE GUERNSEYS, EVEN IF THEY ARE PLAYED OUT, MILK-WISE. SORRY, BUT THEY JUST DON'T RING MY BELL.

ANYBODY OUT THERE GOT A COW YOU WANT TO FLING? TROT HER ON OVER. CICELY, ALASKA. CHRIS-IN-THE-MORNING ON KBHR.

Naturally, Cicely and environs respond with some curiosity to Chris's announcement that he's building the giant catapult to fling a cow to its death. To Shelly, "totally bitchin'" eighteen-year-old former Miss Northwest Passage, he explains it this way:

WELL, YOU KNOW, SHELLY, THE HUMAN SOUL CHOOSES TO EXPRESS ITSELF IN A PROFOUND PROFUSION OF WAYS. WHAT I'M DEALING WITH IS THE AESTHETICS OF THE TRANSITORY. IN THIS PARTICULAR EXHIBITION, THE FLEETING NATURE OF THE PIECE ITSELF BECOMES A COMMENT ON MORTALITY. LIKE THE TEMPORARY INSTALLATIONS OF CHRISTO, I'M CREATING TOMORROW'S MEMORIES. AND, AS MEMORIES, MY IMAGES REMAIN AS IMMORTAL AS ART WHICH IS CONCRETE.

Unfortunately, that particular transitory moment has already been memorialized. When Ed mentions that cows had been flung in a Monty Python movie, Chris is crestfallen.

Maurice airily advises that Chris just fling something else, which only adds to Chris's growing depression.

> YOU DON'T UNDERSTAND. IT'S BEEN DONE. REPE-TITION IS THE DEATH OF ART.
>
> YOU THINK INSPIRATION GROWS ON TREES? CRE-ATIVITY'S NOT A FORMULA, MAURICE. YOU CAN'T MIX IT IN A BEAKER. AN ARTIST HAS TO GO DEEP DOWN INTO HIS GUTS AND PULL IT OUT.

At about that same time Maggie's mother, who's arrived in Cicely to announce that she and Maggie's father are divorcing, accidentally burns down her daughter's house.

Later, as he pokes around the smoking rubble with Maggie, Chris rediscovers his creative vision.

> LOOK AT THIS—THIS IS BEAUTIFUL! WE ARE STANDING AT THE CENTER OF PRIMORDIAL OOZE. IT'S LIKE THE WORLD AT THE DAWN OF CREATION . . .
>
> THIS IS THE ANSWER, RIGHT HERE. DESTRUCTION AND CREATION. THE SCARRED BATTLEFIELD OF LIFE. FROM THE ASHES RISES THE PHOENIX! FROM THE SKIN RISES A NEW SNAKE!
>
> YOU LOOK AND YOU LOOK AND IT'S DARK AND YOU DON'T EVEN KNOW WHAT YOU'RE LOOKING FOR, OR IF YOU'LL EVEN SEE IT, OR IF IT EVEN EXISTS. AND THEN, ALL OF A SUDDEN. . . .

You find a piano to fling.
All of Cicely turns out to watch Chris do it.

WELCOME, EVERYBODY! WELCOME! THANK YOU ALL FOR SHOWING UP.

I'VE BEEN OUT HERE FOR SOME DAYS, GROPING MY WAY ALONG, TRYING TO REALIZE MY VISION. I WAS CONCENTRATING SO HARD ON THE VISION, I LOST SIGHT. COME TO FIND OUT, IT'S NOT THE VISION. IT'S NOT THE VISION AT ALL.

IT'S THE GROPING, PEOPLE—IT'S THE GROPING, THE YEARNING, THE PUSHING FORTH.

I WAS FIXATED ON THAT FLYING COW. THEN WHEN ED SAID MONTY PYTHON HAD ALREADY PAINTED THAT PICTURE, I THOUGHT I WAS THROUGH. I HAD TO LET GO OF THAT COW TO SEE ALL THE OTHER POSSIBILITIES, EVEN THOUGH THAT WAS FRIGHTENING, BECAUSE I DIDN'T KNOW WHERE I WAS HEADED, AND I DIDN'T KNOW WHERE I'D COME OUT—SEE?

I'D LIKE TO THANK MAURICE FOR HELPING ME LET GO OF THAT COW. THANK YOU, MAURICE, FOR PLAY-ING APOLLO TO MY DIONYSUS IN ART'S CARTESIAN DIALECTIC. ED—YOU TOO. THE TRUTH SHALL SET US FREE. AND MAGGIE, FOR SHARING THE DEVASTATION OF HER LIFE, WITHOUT WHICH TODAY'S FLING WOULD NOT BE POSSIBLE.

AS KIERKEGAARD SAID SO WELL, "THE SELF IS ONLY THAT WHICH IT IS IN THE PROCESS OF BECOMING." ART, SAME THING. JAMES JOYCE HAD SOMETHING TO SAY ABOUT IT TOO:

"WELCOME, O LIFE! I GO TO ENCOUNTER FOR THE MILLIONTH TIME THE REALITY OF EXPERIENCE AND

TO FORGE IN THE SMITHY OF MY SOUL THE UNCRE-ATED CONSCIENCE OF MY RACE."

AND SO, WE ARE HERE TO FLING SOME <u>THING</u>, AN IMAGE THAT BUBBLED UP OUT OF THE COLLECTIVE UNCONSCIOUS OF OUR COMMUNITY.

WHAT I'VE LEARNED, PEOPLE, AND THIS IS ABSOLUTELY KEY: IT'S NOT THE THING YOU FLING, IT'S THE FLING ITSELF.

LET'S FLING SOMETHING!

7
CICELY

IT'S SIX-FIFTEEN, CHINOOKS. RISE AND SHINE. I CAN SMELL THOSE GRIDDLE CAKES. MOM'S SQUEEZING THE VALENCIAS. DAD'S GETTING READY FOR WORK. TODAY IS FAMILY DAY HERE ON CHRIS-IN-THE-MORNING. LET'S MAKE A SPECIAL EFFORT TO DO SOMETHING NICE FOR OUR PARENTS.

Another perfect day in that Alaskan paradise, where—regardless of the season or the occasion—Cicely's radios always seem to be tuned to Chris-in-the-Morning.

ON CICELY'S SOCIAL CALENDAR: TRAPPED AS WE ARE ON THAT MERRY-GO-ROUND OF TIME, WE'VE CIRCLED AROUND ONCE AGAIN TO THE ANNUAL CICELY, ALASKA, BIRTHDAY-BASH EXTRAVAGANZA.

YES, TOMORROW'S FOUNDER'S DAY, WHEN WE GET TOGETHER AT THE CHURCH TO MARK THAT SPECIAL DAY BACK IN 1932 WHEN CICELY AND ROSLYN STALLED OUT HERE ON THE CUSP OF THE NEW ALASKAN RIVIERA AND DECIDED TO MAKE THE BEST OF A BAD SITUATION.

NOW, NOBODY REALLY KNOWS FOR SURE WHAT HAPPENED IN THAT STALLED CAR OUT IN THE WOODS WITH OUR FOUNDER, CICELY, AND HER VERY SPECIAL FRIEND, ROSLYN. ALL ALONE, A LITTLE HOME-SICK, COUPLA SLUGS OUT OF ROSLYN'S HIP FLASK, ONE THING LEADS TO ANOTHER . . .

HEY, WE'VE ALL SEEN CICELY'S PICTURE. SURE, SHE'S ON THE HEAVYSET SIDE, A LITTLE JOWLY, BUT VERY ATTRACTIVE IN A MARGARET THATCHER WAY. I COULD SEE SOMEONE WANTING TO DO IT WITH HER.

NOT <u>ME,</u> BUT YOU GET INTO AREAS OF ATTRACTION AND WE START TALKING SERIOUS MYSTERY.

AND WHILE WE'RE TALKING ABOUT MYSTERY, THE VIDEO SOCIETY CONTINUES DEATH AND DEVAS-TATION MONTH THIS WEDNESDAY AT RUTH-ANNE'S LIBRARY. TONIGHT'S SELECTION, <u>PILEUP ON HIGH-WAY 10,</u> IS ON LOAN FROM THE PRIVATE COLLECTION OF ED.

Of course, through the magic of video, by the time we finally get to meet them, both Cicely and Roslyn turn out to be quite pretty, after all.

LET'S JUST SAY THEY WERE VERY, VERY CLOSE, AND LEAVE IT AT THAT. THEY HAD SOMETHING, AND THEY WERE LUCKY TO HAVE IT. AND WE WERE LUCKY TO HAVE THEM, FOLKS. CICELY AND ROSLYN CREATED THE PLACE WE CALL HOME SWEET HOME. SO REMEMBER THEM HOWEVER YOU WANT. THEY WON'T MIND. THEY'RE DEAD.

BUT FOLKS . . . DO REMEMBER THEM.

And one more thing, folks: with each season, Cicely flowers with some civic oddity, from the Christmas Raven pageant to the spring baroque collective madness that is the annual Running of the Bulls, so don't forget to stay tuned to K-BEAR for the latest psychic-weather report . . .

SPRING IS ABOUT TO SPRING—PERSEPHONE'S COMING BACK. AND HERE IN CICELY, THE ICE IS GROANING, ABOUT TO BREAK WITH THAT EXQUISITE, DEAFENING ROAR. IT'S A TIME FOR MADNESS. A TIME FOR OUR FANGS TO COME DOWN AND OUR EYES TO GLAZE OVER SO THE BEAST IN US CAN SING WITH UNMITI-GATED JOY. YES, ECSTASY, I WELCOME THEE.

THE LUNAR ECLIPSE IS A TRIFLE IN COMPARISON, SANTA ANA WINDS AIN'T NOTHING, THE MISTRAL IS JUST A BREEZE. NONE OF THEM CAN HOLD A CANDLE TO OUR EPIC, MIND-ALTERING, PERSONALITY-TRANS-FORMING CICELY MELTDOWN.

AS A SIGN OF THE TIMES, RICHARD SURNAMPOW HAS REPORTED HIS HUNDRED-WATT AUDIO COM-PONENT SYSTEM WITH DOUBLE-CASSETTE DECK AND FIFTEEN-KEY REMOTE CONTROL HAS BEEN STOLEN. TOUGH BREAK, DICK, BUT . . . IT HAPPENS THIS TIME OF YEAR. SO, SIT BACK, RELAX, AND GO WITH THE FLOW.

Going with the flow isn't always easy, though, especially when it comes to getting along with your loved ones. Or getting through an Alaskan winter.

SNOW USUALLY MAKES ME MELLOW—CURL-UP-IN-THE-CORNER TIME, SLOW DOWN AND SMELL THE FURNITURE.

BUT TODAY, IT JUST MAKES ME . . . WET.

WHAT IS IT ABOUT POSSESSING THINGS? WHY DO WE FEEL THE NEED TO OWN WHAT WE LOVE? AND WHY DO WE BECOME SUCH JERKS WHEN WE DO?

WE'VE ALL BEEN THERE. YOU WANT SOMETHING, YOU POSSESS IT—AND BY POSSESSING IT, YOU LOSE IT.

YOU WIN THE GIRL OF YOUR DREAMS, AND THE FIRST THING YOU DO IS TRY TO CHANGE HER. THAT LITTLE THING SHE DID WITH HER HAIR, THE CLOTHES SHE WEARS, THE WAY SHE CHEWS HER GUM. BEFORE LONG, WHAT YOU LIKED, WHAT YOU'VE CHANGED, WHAT YOU DON'T LIKE—IT ALL RUNS TOGETHER, LIKE SNOWFLAKES IN THE WIND.

Sometimes Chris's enthusiasms are definitely against the flow, as in the episode entitled "Dateline: Cicely." Chris buys into Holling's bar, The Brick, and promptly begins touting his "improvements" on-air.

While Chris uncharacteristically makes a jerk of himself, the rest of the citizenry is tramping around the woods, blithely conversing with the trees as the result of an exposé that appears in the *Cicely News and World Telegram,* the flagship of Maurice's communications empire. The story, entitled "Amazing Find in Tundra!! Trees That Talk!" carries the byline of "Anon." But the author, it turns out, is none other than gourmet chef, part-time investigative reporter, and all-around misanthropic sociopath Adam.

LITTLE WEATHER ADVISORY FOR ALL OF YOU OUT THERE CONVERSING WITH OUR LOCAL FLORA: STORM FRONT DUE IN FROM THE NORTHEAST. WHY NOT COME IN FROM THE COLD AND WARM YOURSELVES WITH A BOWL OF HOMEMADE CHILI AT THE BRICK? A HEARTY HELPING FOR A MEASLY BUCK SEVENTY-FIVE . . . OR MAYBE YOU'VE GOT BETTER THINGS TO DO.

TONIGHT'S ANGLO-SAXON NIGHT AT THE BRICK, OUR SALUTE TO OUR SOGGY FOREBEARS FROM THE SCEPTERED ISLE. WE'RE FEATURING THE FIRST ANNUAL ARROWHEAD TAG-TEAM DART CHAMPIONSHIP . . .

SEEMED LIKE A GOOD IDEA AT THE TIME. GUESS WE'LL GIVE IT A TRY.

WHO'D HAVE THOUGHT OUR SLEEPY LITTLE HAMLET BORDERS THE MOST UNUSUAL BOTANICAL FIND OF THE CENTURY? BUT DON'T TAKE MY WORD FOR IT. PICK UP YOUR OWN COPY OF THE <u>CICELY NEWS AND WORLD TELEGRAM</u> TODAY AND READ ABOUT BIZARRE BUT TRUE DISCOVERIES IN A FOREST PRIMEVAL THAT TIME FORGOT. IT'S ALL IN THE <u>CICELY NEWS AND WORLD TELEGRAM,</u> THE PRIDE AND PULSE OF THE BOROUGH OF ARROWHEAD COUNTY.

AND TO SWAP STORIES ABOUT OUR LOQUACIOUS LODGEPOLES, WHY NOT STOP IN AT CICELY'S FAVORITE WATERING HOLE, THE BRICK, HOME OF THE NEW PTARMIGAN PIZZA. ENJOY YOUR STATE BIRD WITH MOZZARELLA, TOMATO, AND BASIL, ALL ON A CORN-FLOUR CRUST. AND TONIGHT'S T. S. ELIOT NIGHT AT THE BRICK. YOURS TRULY, CHRIS STEVENS, WILL BE MANNING THE PUMPS. THERE'LL BE NICKEL BEER FOR THE FIRST FIFTY CUSTOMERS WHO CAN RECITE THE OPENING LINE OF "THE LOVE SONG OF J. ALFRED PRUFROCK." NO CRIB SHEETS.

Chris has always had a complex relationship with saloons. On the one hand, as he tells Maurice, he does require a good tavern, always open, nearby; on the other, as he admits to Holling, he's not cut out to own one.

LAST NIGHT? I COULDN'T BREATHE. I HAD TO LEAVE A BAR FOR THE FIRST TIME IN MY LIFE. IT'S WEIRD. I LOVED <u>YOUR</u> BAR, HOLLING, BUT WHEN IT BECAME <u>MY</u> BAR, ALL I COULD SEE WERE THINGS I WANTED TO CHANGE. AND THEN LAST NIGHT, WHEN I STEPPED BACK TO LOOK AT IT, I GOT THAT AWFUL FEELING IN THE PIT OF MY STOMACH—YOU KNOW, WHEN YOU'VE LOST THAT LOVING FEELING, BUT YOU'RE STILL TRYING TO HANG ON? I CAN'T ENJOY MYSELF IN THE BRICK ANYMORE.

AND WHAT IT'S DONE TO MY HEAD IS TRULY STRANGE. THINKING ABOUT PROFIT MARGIN, RETURN ON INVESTMENT, MAKING PEOPLE USE COASTERS . . . COASTERS! WHERE'D <u>THAT</u> COME FROM?

I REALLY THOUGHT OWNING A BAR WAS GOING TO BE IT FOR ME. BUT I GUESS THERE ARE TWO TYPES OF PEOPLE IN THIS WORLD, HOLLING: OWNERS AND RENTERS. I'M A RENTER. I HAVE TO GET OUT.

Yes, even philosophers get the blues.

SINCE HOLLING CLOSED THE BRICK, I'VE BEEN FEELING A KIND OF WITHDRAWAL, SOMETHING ON THE ORDER OF GRIEF. THE BRICK IS HOME, MOTHER, SOURCE OF BREWSKIS AND HOT MEALS. I WANT BREAKFAST, I HIT THE BRICK. I FINISH MY SHOW, I HIT THE BRICK. LUNCHTIME ROLLS AROUND. . . . SO YOU SEE, WITHOUT A BAR—THE NOISE, THE SMELL, THE TUNES ON THE JUKEBOX—I HAVE NO HOME. NO PLACE TO HANG MY HAT, NO POT TO PEE IN.

"I FELT A FUNERAL, IN MY BRAIN,
AND MOURNERS TO AND FRO
KEPT TREADING—TREADING—TILL IT SEEMED
THAT SENSE WAS BREAKING THROUGH—

AND WHEN THEY ALL WERE SEATED,
A SERVICE, LIKE A DRUM—
KEPT BEATING—BEATING—TILL I THOUGHT
MY MIND WAS GOING NUMB— . . ."

I THINK WHAT EMILY HAD IN MIND WHEN SHE PENNED THOSE LINES SUMS UP THE KIND OF DAY I'VE BEEN HAVING. EMOTIONAL WEATHER REPORT: CLOUDY WITH CHANCE OF RAIN UNTIL LATER IN THE WEEK WHEN THE BRICK REOPENS.

Just as the good times do, life's little adversities require a soundtrack, as Chris-in-the-Morning well knows. Sometimes, all it takes is for one of Cicely's citizens to call in and make a request . . .

WELCOME BACK TO OUR SPECIAL BLUES-IN-THE-NIGHT EDITION OF CHRIS-IN-THE-MORNING. WE'RE ENTERTAINING ANY AND ALL REQUESTS FOR MUSIC TO GO WITH THOSE EXCEPTIONAL MOMENTS IN LIFE WHEN YOU JUST WANT TO CRAWL IN A HOLE, SHRIVEL UP, AND DIE.

WHY? BECAUSE SOMETIMES YOU HAVE TO LIE DOWN WITH YOUR PAIN. AS JUNG SAID, "THERE IS NO COMING TO CONSCIOUSNESS WITHOUT PAIN." SO LET'S GET CONSCIOUS, CICELY.

Getting conscious is a growth industry in tiny Cicely. Maybe that's why Chris prefers Alaska to just about anywhere else.

WELL, I'LL TELL YOU; I TRIED JUST ABOUT EVERY ONE OF THE LOWER FORTY-EIGHT, BUT—I DON'T KNOW—THEM AND ME, WE JUST CLASH.

THE THING THAT MAKES ME AND ALASKA WORK—

IT'S LIKE THAT STORY ROBERT BLY TELLS ABOUT THE FOREST WHERE HUNTERS GO BUT THEY NEVER COME BACK; AND THEN OTHER HUNTERS GO SEARCHING FOR THEM, BUT THEY DON'T COME BACK EITHER. THEN ONE DAY THIS LONE YOUNG HUNTER APPEARS, AND HE ASKS IF THERE'S ANYWHERE DANGEROUS AROUND, AND EVERYONE TELLS HIM ABOUT THE FOREST, BUT THEY WARN HIM THAT NO ONE COMES BACK. BUT HE SAYS, NO, NO, THAT'S JUST WHAT HE HAD IN MIND.

SO HE TAKES HIS DOG—JUST HIS DOG, NO OTHER PEOPLE, THAT'S IMPORTANT—AND HE GOES INTO THE FOREST. AND HE WALKS AND WALKS, AND SUDDENLY HE COMES TO THIS POND, AND THIS HAND COMES UP OUT OF THE POND, GRABS HIS DOG, AND PULLS HIM UNDER. DOG IS HISTORY. AND THE HUNTER DOESN'T GET UPSET OR HYSTERICAL OR ANYTHING. HE JUST LOOKS UP TOWARD THE HEAVENS AND HE SAYS, "THIS MUST BE THE PLACE."

THAT'S HOW I FEEL ABOUT ALASKA.

PART II

OPINIONS AND OBSERVATIONS, A-Z

AGING

HERE IN THE WESTERN WORLD, WE HAVE THIS MORBID FEAR OF AGING, THIS SIMPLISTIC GLORIFICATION OF YOUTH. IN THE ORIENT, OLD AGE IS REVERED—IT'S THE TOP OF THE HEAP, A TIME OF WISDOM AND INFLUENCE.

PEOPLE IMPOSE ALL THESE CHRONOLOGICAL IMPERATIVES ON THEMSELVES. THEY DON'T MAKE A MILLION BUCKS BY THE TIME THEY'RE THIRTY, THEY'RE JUMPING OFF BRIDGES.

ALASKA

THERE'S A FINE LINE BETWEEN THE WILD AND THE TAME. BETWEEN ALASKA AND US. ME—I'VE GOTTA HAVE MY MUSIC, MY BOOKS. BUT NO MATTER HOW URBANE WE HUMANS BECOME, SOMETHING IN US STILL LONGS FOR THE VIRGIN FOREST.

THIS LAST GREAT GASP OF WILDERNESS . . . THIS SHAGGY BARBARIAN EARTH. NORTH TO THE FUTURE! OR IS IT THE PAST?

ALIENATION (SEE ALSO SEX)

IT'S THE "OTHER." THINK OF CONCENTRIC CIRCLES:
THE INNER CIRCLE IS OURSELF. THE NEXT, THE FAMILY;
THEN THE TRIBE. THEN THE NEIGHBORING TRIBE,
AND SO ON. THE FARTHER AWAY YOU GO, THE MORE
FOREIGN THINGS GET. PEOPLE IN THE OUTER CIRCLES,
THEY BECOME THE "OTHER."

AMERICA (SEE ALSO DEMOCRACY)

WE WERE OUTCASTS, SCUM, THE WRETCHED DETRITUS OF A HOSTILE, AGING WORLD. WE CAME HERE AND PAVED ROADS, BUILT INDUSTRIES, POWERFUL PRODIGIOUS INSTITUTIONS.

OF COURSE, ALONG THE WAY WE EXTERMINATED UNTOLD INDIGENOUS CULTURES, ENSLAVED GENERATIONS OF AFRICANS—BASICALLY STAINED OUR STAR-SPANGLED BANNER WITH A HOST OF SINS THAT CAN NEVER BE WASHED CLEAN.

ARBITRARY PREFERENCES

I DRAW THE LINE AT FRECKLES. IT'S NOT A VALUE JUDGMENT. FOR YOU IT'S AN ACCIDENT OF BIRTH, FOR ME IT'S AN ARBITRARY PREFERENCE.

ARCHERY

IN KYUDO PHILOSOPHY, YOU DON'T AIM—YOU BECOME ONE WITH THE TARGET. THEN, IN FACT, THERE'S NOTHING TO AIM AT. I FIND IT WORKS WELL WITH WOMEN, TOO. GIVE IT A TRY.

ART (SEE ALSO SLAM DANCING)

REPETITION IS THE DEATH OF ART.

AURORA BOREALIS
(SEE ALSO NORTHERN LIGHTS)

DON'T QUOTE ME ON THIS, BUT I THINK HIGH-SPEED ELECTRONS AND PROTONS FROM THE SUN ARE

TRAPPED IN THE VAN ALLEN RADIATION BELT AND THEN CHANNELED THROUGH THE POLAR REGIONS BY THE EARTH'S MAGNETIC FIELD WHERE THEY COLLIDE WITH OTHER PARTICLES TO CREATE A BRILLIANT LUMINOSITY.

AUTUMN

YOU KNOW, IT'S HARD NOT TO BECOME REFLECTIVE DURING THE THREE MONTHS LEADING TO THE WINTER SOLSTICE. IF WINTER IS SLUMBER, AND SPRING IS BIRTH . . . AND SUMMER? SUMMER'S LIFE. SO, THEN AUTUMN ROUNDS OUT TO BE A REFLECTION. IT'S A TIME OF YEAR WHEN THE LEAVES ARE DOWN, THE HARVEST'S IN, THE PERENNIALS ARE GONE—MOTHER EARTH'S JUST CLOSED UP THE DRAPES ON ANOTHER YEAR, AND IT'S TIME TO REFLECT ON WHAT'S COME BEFORE.

BEHAVIOR

I'M ALL FOR RASH BEHAVIOR.

BEARS (SEE DEATH; SPRING)

BEING THERE

I THINK WHEN YOU ARE SOMEWHERE, YOU OUGHTA BE THERE, 'CAUSE IT'S NOT ABOUT HOW LONG YOU STAY IN A PLACE. IT'S ABOUT WHAT YOU DO WHILE

YOU'RE THERE. AND—WHEN YOU GO, WILL THE PLACE WHERE YOU'VE BEEN BE ANY BETTER OFF FOR YOUR HAVING BEEN THERE?

BIORHYTHMIC VALLEYS, SNAPPING OUT OF

THERE'S NO GETTING AROUND THE FACT THAT EVERY NOW AND THEN WE ALL NEED A PUMP, SOMETHING TO MAKE US JUMP OUT OF BED AND GREET THE DAWN WITH A COSMIC "HOWDY."

BROWSING

BROWSE. IT'S GOOD FOR THE SOUL.

BULLS, ANNUAL RUNNING OF THE
(SEE ALSO NAKED RUNNING)

A CICELIAN TRADITION. IT WARMS UP ONCE YOU GET GOING.

CAGES (SEE STAYING PUT)

CARPENTRY

I'M AN ACE SANDER—GET INTO A ZEN THING.

CAUSE AND EFFECT

YOU PUT STUFF OUT INTO THE UNIVERSE, IT UNLEASHES A CHAIN OF EVENTS. YOU PLAY, YOU PAY.

CHRISTMAS IN CICELY

THERE'S NOTHING LIKE THE SIGHT OF A BEAUTIFUL,

BLACK-AS-PITCH RAVEN TO FILL YOU WITH THE
CHRISTMAS SPIRIT.

CHRISTMAS CAROLS

I HEAR CHRISTMAS CAROLS—ALL THOSE TOO-
HUMAN VOICES ASCENDING TO HEAVEN IN A HAR-
MONIC PYRAMID OF SOUND—AND I GET VERY
ZONED, VERY LIGHT IN MY GALOSHES. THAT HAPPEN
TO YOU?

CICELY, INDIGENOUS FLORA OF

OUR TREES HAVE QUIT THEIR HOWLING. END OF A
CROWD-PLEASING PHENOMENON FOR US, PERHAPS,
BUT RESUMPTION OF BUSINESS AS USUAL FOR THEM.
LIFE IN THE SLOW LANE. AS IT SHOULD BE. IF OUR
TIMBER WERE TO SPEAK AGAIN, MY GUESS IS IT
WOULD SAY, "HEY, PEOPLE—ENOUGH."

CICELY—A K-BEAR PUBLIC SERVICE ANNOUNCEMENT

COCKADOODLE-DOO, CICELY. RISE AND SHINE. IT'S
ME-IN-THE-MORNING ON K-BEAR AND I'M LOOKING
DOWN MAIN STREET, AND YOU CANNOT BELIEVE
WHAT I'M SEEING. A GUY WITH A TOILET-PAPER FACE,
OKAY? THERE'S ONE WITH NO FACE AT ALL. MAN!
THERE GOES TWO HANDS—THEY'RE WALKING,
THEY'RE WAVING AT ME, PEOPLE. HEY—HOWDY,
HANDS!

THIS IS GOOD. THIS IS VERY GOOD. THIS IS THE PAR-ALLEL UNIVERSE. THE ONE WHERE TOASTERS TALK AND SLURPIE STRAWS WALK. IT'S ALICE IN WONDER-LAND, YOU KNOW? THE OTHER SIDE OF ROGER RABBIT. BUT THIS IS NO CARTOON. OKAY?

HEY, I'M NOT MAKING THIS UP. GOT A FLYER HERE SAYS THEY'RE ENRICO BELLATI AND HIS NEW PER-CEPTION PLAYERS AND THEY WELCOME ONE AND ALL TO AN EVENING OF AWE AND EXPECTATION. PEOPLE'S PARK, NEXT TO THE BRICK. BE THERE—OR YOUR TEAPOT MAY NEVER TALK TO YOU AGAIN.

CICELY—ANOTHER K-BEAR PUBLIC SERVICE ANNOUNCEMENT

A K-BEAR CAUTION TO ALL OUR LOYAL LISTENERS: THIS EVENING MARKS THE END OF OUR COLLECTIVE MIDSUMMER NIGHT'S DREAM. SO GET THOSE PUPILS READY TO DILATE BECAUSE, FOR THE FIRST TIME IN A LONG TIME, OUR CONSTANT COMPANION, OLD SOL, IS EMBARKING ON A QUICKIE VACATION, A SHORT DIP BENEATH THE HORIZON, A JUNKET TO WHICH-EVER CLUB MED ACCOMMODATES MEDIUM-SIZED STARS. AND WHILE HE'S GONE, I WANT ALL OF YOU OUT THERE TO BE ALERT, BE CAREFUL, AND PLEASE, PLEASE, PLEASE—THREE TIMES PLEASE—TURN ON YOUR HEADLIGHTS.

CICELY—ONE MORE PUBLIC SERVICE ANNOUNCEMENT

ED WANTS TO REMIND EVERYBODY IN THE FILM

SOCIETY THAT THERE WILL BE A SHOWING OF <u>THE</u> <u>SORROW AND THE PITY</u> TOMORROW NIGHT, AND YOU SHOULD REMEMBER TO BRING LOTS OF SNACKS BECAUSE IT'S FIVE HOURS LONG. FIVE HOURS? AND MRS. FAST CLOUD WANTS WHOEVER BORROWED THE BALL BLOWER FROM THE BINGO HALL TO RETURN IT . . . OR THERE WON'T BE ANYTHING TO DO BUT GO TO <u>THE SORROW AND THE PITY.</u>

   SORRY, ED.

CICELY—YET ANOTHER PUBLIC SERVICE ANNOUNCEMENT

TRICK OR TREAT, MONEY OR EATS TO OUR K-BEAR

LISTENERS FROM YOURS TRULY, CHRIS STEVENS, ON THIS ALL HALLOWS EVE. I'M SITTING HERE ENJOYING THE FLICKERING LIGHT OF A JACK-O'-LANTERN, COURTESY OF MY OLD BUDDY HOLLING VINCOEUR, WHOSE PUMPKIN CARVING HAS WON HIM FAME FROM NOME TO SEATTLE.

AND HERE'S A LITTLE POLICE BULLETIN FOR THOSE OF YOU PLANNING ANY EGG THROWING, OUTHOUSE TIPPING, OR OTHER MISCHIEF. BE ADVISED: ALASKA'S OWN INSPECTOR JAVERT, OFFICER BARBARA SEMANSKI, IS ON THE PROWL. HAVING SUCCUMBED TO THE BLANDISHMENTS OF LOVE, SHE'S GIVEN MAURICE A REPRIEVE AND IS CURRENTLY BEING SQUIRED SOMEWHERE IN THE VICINITY. CONGRATS, MAURICE. AND THE REST OF YOU—BEWARE.

CICELY—TRAFFIC REPORT

MAGGIE O'CONNELL JUST DROVE DOWN MAIN STREET. TOO FAST.

CICELY—TEMPERATURE REPORT

OUTSIDE TEMP'S BACK TO NORMAL. INSIDE TEMP MIGHT TAKE A FEW DAYS TO RETURN TO PSYCHIC STABILITY.

CICELY—WEATHER REPORT

THE WEATHER HAS BEEN STRANGE. THE WOLVES ARE ACTING LOONY BECAUSE OF THE MOONLIGHT.

COMING OF AGE

YOU WERE APPLE JUICE, NOW YOU'RE CIDER.

CONFUCIUS, ENTIRE PHILOSOPHY OF (SEE RECIPROCITY)

CONTROL, ILLUSION OF BEING IN

YOU'RE NOT. NONE OF US IS. WE'RE ATOMS, DUST, YET BOUND TO ONE ANOTHER IN PATTERNS WE CAN NEVER COMPREHEND. JUST ACCEPT IT.

CRANES (SEE ALSO STAYING PUT)

CRANES ARE CARRYING SOME HEAVY MYSTICAL BAGGAGE. ICONS OF HAPPINESS AND FIDELITY. THE VIETNAMESE BELIEVE THEY CART SOULS UP TO HEAVEN ON THEIR WINGS.

WATCHING 'EM WING IT UP THERE, IT MAKES ME FEEL EVEN MORE EARTHBOUND, LIKE THE FLIGHTLESS BIRD I AM.

CREATION (SEE ALSO PICASSO)

EVERY ACT OF CREATION IS AN ACT OF DESTRUCTION.

CULTURAL RELATIVISM

ALL I CAN TELL YOU IS THAT CUSTOMS VARY. CERTAIN PLAINS INDIANS, FOR EXAMPLE, WOULD INSERT AN IRON BARB UNDER THE FLESH AND RAISE STRIPES

LEADING FROM THE BACK OF THE HAND TO THE SHOULDER.

DEAD PERSON, UNKNOWN

WE FEEL A KIND OF CONNECTION TO THIS MAN. WE DON'T KNOW HIM—BUT IN A WAY WE DO. IT'S LIKE HE'S A STILL POND. YOU KNOW, WE SEE OUR OWN REFLECTION.

DEATH

YOU KNOW, AT THE SAME TIME OUR CRO-MAGNON ANCESTORS STARTED BURYING THEMSELVES, THEY STARTED DOING THE SAME THING WITH BEARS. WHAT DOES THAT MEAN? WHAT'S GOING ON HERE?

THE BIG BANG OF THE HUMAN PSYCHE, THE RECOGNITION OF DEATH. WE SAW DEATH AND DID WHAT NO OTHER ANIMAL HAD DONE BEFORE: WE DEALT WITH IT. WE HIT ON THE IDEA THAT DEATH WAS NOT THE END, THAT IT WAS JUST A PASSAGE. THAT'S WHY WE GAVE MR. BEAR A PROPER FUNERAL, SO THAT HE WOULDN'T COME BACK PISSED.

WE WERE TRYING TO MAKE SENSE OF THE UNKNOWABLE, WHAT JOE CAMPBELL CALLS THE AWAKENING OF AWE.

DEGREES (SEE LEGITIMACY—LICENSES)

DEMOCRACY (SEE ALSO AMERICA)

FRIENDS, ROMANS, REGISTERED VOTERS, LEND ME YOUR EARS! MY HEART IS POUNDING, DANCING TO

THE DRUM OF A FREE PEOPLE, A CITY ON A HILL, E PLURIBUS UNUM. I FEEL AT ONE WITH WHITMAN, SHEPHERD OF THE GREAT UNWASHED. "O DEMOCRA-CY! NEAR AT HAND TO YOU A THROAT IS NOW INFLATING ITSELF AND JOYFULLY SINGING."

DEMOCRACY, GETTING INVOLVED IN (SEE ALSO BEING THERE)

DEMOCRACY IS NOT A SPECTATOR SPORT, MY FRIENDS. BE WORTHY OF YOUR HERITAGE. AS JUSTICE HOLMES REMARKED, "IT IS REQUIRED OF A MAN THAT HE SHOULD SHARE THE PASSION AND ACTION OF HIS TIME AT PERIL OF BEING JUDGED NOT TO HAVE LIVED."

'NUFF SAID. BE THERE.

DESPAIR, AVOIDING IT

THROW ON THOSE PSYCHIC RAINCOATS! PULL UP THE COLLAR! THINK ON SUNNIER CLIMES.

DESTINY

A MAN HAS TO LIVE OUT HIS OWN DESTINY, NOT SOMEONE ELSE'S.

DIVORCE

DIVORCES AREN'T PERFORMED. THEY'RE HANDLED.

DREAMS (SEE ALSO JUNG, CARL)

"THE UNCONSCIOUS IS REVEALED THROUGH THE

IMAGERY OF OUR DREAMS, WHICH EXPRESS OUR INNERMOST FEARS, DESIRES, AND PSYCHIC PERCEPTIONS." I THINK IT WAS JUNG. OR MAYBE VINCENT PRICE.

ELECTION, NIXON V. MCGOVERN

THIS WAS 1972, FOLKS. NOT A WHOLE LOT OF DOUBT ABOUT THE OUTCOME.

ELECTIONS, SYSTEM OF (SEE ALSO DEMOCRACY)

IT'S NOT PERFECT, BUT IT'S THE BEST SYSTEM ANYONE'S COME UP WITH.

ENGINES

WHY DO WE SAY "SHE?" MAYBE BECAUSE AN ENGINE IS BOTH TEMPERAMENTAL AND POWERFUL.

ENNUI, EXAMPLE OF

IT'S ALL THE SAME TO ME. THE SAME FACES, THE SAME CONVERSATIONS. I KNOW WHAT PEOPLE ARE GOING TO SAY BEFORE THEY EVEN OPEN THEIR MOUTHS. WORK, EAT, SLEEP. WORK, EAT, SLEEP. I SEE THE DAYS STRETCHING OUT IN FRONT OF ME LIKE AN ENDLESS BODHIDARMA MEDITATION.

OH, I COULD MOVE TO A NEW PLACE—NEW YORK, PARIS—START OVER AGAIN. THINGS WOULD BE FRESH AND NEW . . . FOR A WHILE. THEN WHAT? MOVE ON AGAIN? WHAT'S THE POINT? LOVE. . . ?

FACTS (SEE TRUTH)

FOCUS, LACK OF

LACK OF FOCUS: INCREASES ANXIETY, DECREASES PLEASURE.

FRIENDSHIP (SEE also GUILT, EXAMPLE OF)

NOT THAT I'M INCAPABLE OF STABBING A FRIEND IN THE BACK. I'M AS GUILTY AS ANYBODY. BUT I'M NOT PREPARED TO DO IT AT THIS PARTICULAR TIME.

FURTIVE MIND

LIKE THE WATERS OF THE BIG MUDDY, IT'S HARD TO SEE TO THE BOTTOM OF IT. IT'S DEEP WHERE YOU THINK IT'S GONNA BE SHALLOW AND SHALLOW WHERE IT SHOULD BE DEEP.

GOD (SEE ALSO SPRING)

EINSTEIN SAID GOD DOESN'T PLAY DICE WITH THE UNIVERSE, BUT I DON'T KNOW—MAYBE NOT AS A WHOLE, BUT I THINK HE GETS A PRETTY BIG KICK OUT OF MESSIN' IN PEOPLE'S BACKYARDS.

GOOD NEWS/BAD NEWS

THAT NICE OLD CYPRUS TREE AT KIPNUK LAKE FELL OVER AND FLATTENED MY TRAILER LIKE THE PROVERBIAL PANCAKE, CAUSING ME TO JOIN THE GROWING RANKS OF THE NATION'S HOMELESS. THAT'S THE BAD NEWS. THE GOOD NEWS IS I'M LIVING AT THE RADIO STATION AND I NO LONGER HAVE TO CARPOOL TO WORK.

GUILT

A SENSE OF CULPABILITY FOR SOME OFFENSE OR WRONGDOING.

GUILT, EXAMPLE OF

WHAT DID YOU DO? YOU LET A DOG TAKE THE RAP FOR YOUR KID? A HELPLESS DOG THAT CAN'T TALK,

THAT CAN'T DEFEND ITSELF? HOW DO YOU LIVE WITH YOURSELF?

GREAT QUESTION, THE

WHAT DO WOMEN WANT?
SAME THINGS WE DO. ONLY IN PRETTIER COLORS.

HALLOWEEN (SEE CICELY—YET ANOTHER PUBLIC SERVICE ANNOUNCEMENT)

HANGOVER, CURE FOR

TWO RAW EGGS, WORCESTERSHIRE SAUCE, BEEF BOUILLON.
BEST CURE FOR A HANGOVER IS THREE McDONALD'S CHEESEBURGERS AND A JUMBO GULP. BUT WHEN IT'S TOO FAR TO THE GOLDEN ARCHES, YOU MAKE DO WITH WHAT YOU'VE GOT.

HANNAH, DARYL

SHE WAS PRETTY GOOD AS THAT FISH.

HAPPINESS

SOMETIMES IT'S HARD TO AVOID THE HAPPINESS OF OTHERS.

HARLEY-DAVIDSON (SEE HOG—WHY I LIKE IT)

HEALTH, DETERIORATION OF

CONSIDERING THE WHOLESALE TRASHING OF THE PLANET, THE DAILY DEGRADATION WE'VE INFLICTED ON GAIA SINCE THE DAWN OF THE INDUSTRIAL REVOLUTION, IT STRIKES ME AS HARDLY SURPRISING THAT WE'RE ALL WALKING TIME BOMBS, IMMUNO-LOGICALLY SPEAKING, AND THAT SOME OF US WILL GO OFF SOONER THAN OTHERS.

HISTORY, SIGNIFICANCE OF
(SEE ALSO NAPOLEON)

WAS NAPOLEON AT WATERLOO? WOULD IT CHANGE WHAT I HAD FOR BREAKFAST?

HOG—WHY I LIKE IT
(SEE ALSO LOVE, REMEMBRANCE OF; LOSS; TECHNOLOGY)

THE VEHICLE IS JUST A MEANS, AN ENABLER, AN EXTENSION OF YOUR IDEA. AND THAT'S THE JOY OF IT—THE JOURNEY.

HOWEVER, THE GREATER YOUR RAPPORT WITH THE VEHICLE, THE GREATER THE JOY. TAKE MY BIKE. WHY DO I HAVE A HOG? I COULD GET FROM A TO B IN A STATION WAGON, A MINIVAN, A MOPED. . . . BUT A HARLEY-DAVIDSON . . . FOR ME, THAT'S THE ULTI-MATE DRIVING MACHINE.

I THINK, THEREFORE, I DO. I WANNA GO FIFTY—BOOM!—I'M GOING FIFTY. I LIKE THE RUMBLE, I LIKE

THE SMELL OF THE EXHAUST. WHEN I LEAN INTO THE CURVE, SHE'S THERE FOR ME.

PHEW!

HOMOPHOBIA

MEN WHO ARE FREAKED BY HOMOSEXUALS, WELL . . . THEY USUALLY HAVE SOME TENDENCIES IN THAT DIRECTION THEMSELVES.

HUNTING

NOTE THE RISE, THE ARC, THE PREY'S PANIC AT THE PREDATOR'S PRESENCE. LOCK INTO IT. TAKE THE BIRD INSIDE YOU. LINK. LINGER. THEN LASH OUT.

HUNTING, REMORSE OF

THE SHAME OF CAIN SYNDROME. THE FIRST ONE ALWAYS SEEMS LIKE A BROTHER.

JUNG, CARL (SEE ALSO DREAMS; PAIN)

JUNG SAYS DREAMS ARE THE WOOF AND TWEETER OF THE TOTAL SOUND SYSTEM. ABSOLUTELY.

OF COURSE, THERE'S NO WAY TO VERIFY WHETHER JUNG LISTENED TO MUSIC WHILE HE WROTE HIS FAMOUS ESSAY ON THE NATURE OF DREAMS, BUT HE WAS BORN IN BAVARIA, AND SO WAS THE "MOONLIGHT SONATA."

KARMA (SEE ALSO CAUSE AND EFFECT; RECIPROCITY)

KARMA. THE WHEEL. WHAT GOES AROUND COMES AROUND.

KBHR

K-BEAR, 570 ON YOUR AM DIAL. THE RADIO STATION OF THE PEOPLE, BY THE PEOPLE, FOR THE PEOPLE.

KBHR, BROADCAST RADIUS OF

LIKE ONE HAND CLAPPING—THE VOICE OF CICELY REACHING OUT ACROSS THE TUNDRA, OVER THE WAVES, COMMUNING WITH CARIBOU, RIGHT WHALES, MIGRATING PUFFINS.

LEE, BRUCE (SEE LOVE)

LEGITIMACY—LICENSES

WHY THE URGE TO LEGITIMIZE MYSELF WITH A PIECE OF PAPER? TO PUT A POST-IT NOTE ON THIS CHAPTER OF MY LIFE? OR JUST TO SAY TO THE WORLD, "HEY, KILROY STEVENS TOO WAS HERE"?

LEGITIMACY—MARRIAGE

DOES A PIECE OF PAPER MAKE TWO PEOPLE MARRIED? DOES A BAR MITZVAH MAKE THE CHILD A MAN?

LETTERS, DEAR JOHN
(SEE ALSO RELATIONSHIPS, ENDING OF)
YOU THINK YOU KNOW SOMEBODY, AND THEN
THEY BLOW YOU OFF IN A BARELY LEGIBLE LETTER.
YOU SHOULDNT TAKE IT PERSONALLY.

LETTERS, LOVE

THERE'S A WHOLE EPISTOLARY TRADITION—ZELDA AND F. SCOTT, ROBERT BROWNING AND ELIZABETH. TELL HER HOW YOU FEEL . . .

YOU PROBABLY FEEL LIKE YOU CAN HARDLY WAIT TO SEE HER AGAIN. TIME'S PROBABLY CRAWLING BY. YOU'VE PROBABLY LOST YOUR APPETITE.

LONDON, JACK (SEE WHITE FANG AND BUCK)

LOSS

CAN THE LOSS OF A MOTORCYCLE REALLY EQUAL THAT OF A DOG OR A PARAKEET?

LOVE

"LOVE IS LIKE FRIENDSHIP CAUGHT ON FIRE." BRUCE LEE.

LOVE AT FIRST SIGHT

ACTUALLY, IT COULD BE JUST A FORM OF NARCISSISM. I MEAN HOW CAN YOU LOVE SOMEONE IF YOU DON'T KNOW THEM? AREN'T YOU REALLY JUST PROJECTING ONTO THEM THOSE QUALITIES YOU WANT THEM TO HAVE BECAUSE YOU FIND THEM LACKING IN YOURSELF?

LOVE, CAUSE OF

WHAT WAS IT ABOUT HER? WAS IT HER SMILE? THE

WAY SHE CROSSED HER LEGS? THE TURN OF HER ANKLE? THE POIGNANT VULNERABILITY OF THAT SLENDER WRIST? WHAT ARE THOSE ELUSIVE, EPHEMERAL THINGS THAT IGNITE PASSION IN THE HUMAN HEART? WELL, IT'S AN AGE-OLD QUESTION— PERFECT FOOD FOR THOUGHT ON A BRIGHT MID-SUMMER'S NIGHT. HEY, YOU SAID IT BEST, WILL: "LOVE LOOKS NOT WITH THE EYES, BUT WITH THE MIND; AND THEREFORE IS WINGED CUPID PAINTED BLIND."

OH, YEAH.

LOVE, LOST
(SEE ALSO RELATIONSHIPS, ENDING OF)

YOU'RE PROBABLY NOT GOING TO BELIEVE THIS, AND I KNOW YOU PROBABLY FEEL PRETTY TERRIBLE NOW, BUT THIS EXPERIENCE IS GOING TO TRANS-MUTE ITSELF.

YOU DO SOMETHING LIKE THIS, AND IT REALLY TEARS YOU UP—AND EVENTUALLY IT BECOMES ONE OF YOUR FONDEST MEMORIES.

LOVE, REMEMBRANCE OF
(SEE ALSO HOG—WHY I LIKE IT)

I REMEMBER FALLING LIKE THAT ONCE, ONLY FOR ME IT WAS A HARLEY HOG. WHAT A HOT MACHINE!

DAMN BIKE ALMOST KILLED ME, TOO . . . A FUEL-INJECTED RIDE TO HELL.

LOVE, UNREQUITED

YOU THINK ABOUT A WOMAN WHO DOESN'T KNOW YOU'RE THINKING ABOUT HER AND DOESN'T CARE YOU'RE THINKING ABOUT HER . . . AND THAT JUST MAKES YOU THINK ABOUT HER ALL THE MORE.

MARRIAGE, MODELS OF

MARRIED PEOPLE ARE SUPPOSED TO TALK TO EACH OTHER, COMMUNICATE. JUNE AND WARD CLEAVER, LYING IN THEIR SEPARATE TWIN BEDS—HOW MANY TIMES DID JUNE LOOK ACROSS THAT BEDSIDE TABLE AND SAY, "WARD, I THINK YOU'D BETTER HAVE A TALK WITH THE BEAVER?"

THEN AGAIN, IN THE ANIMAL KINGDOM THE MALE AFRICAN BUSH BIRD SHOWS HIS FINEST FEATHERS ONLY DURING MATING RITUALS. ONCE THEY DO THE DEED, HE'S HISTORY.

MATHEMATICS, THE ZEN OF

IT'S THE CIRCLE, THE CONTINUUM, THE MYSTERY OF THE INFINITE.

MONEY

I'D RATHER HAVE MY MONEY HELPING OUT A FRIEND THAN BREEDING IN A BANK SOMEWHERE.

MUSIC, COUNTRY

MAN, YOU'VE GOTTA LOVE COUNTRY MUSIC. IT'S JUST RAW WITH HONESTY AND PASSION. THERE'S HEROES AND VILLAINS, GOOD AND BAD, RIGHT AND WRONG . . .

THE PROTAGONIST STROLLS INTO THE BAR, WHICH HE SEES AS A MICROCOSM OF THE BIG PICTURE. HE

CONTEMPLATES THE MEANING OF HIS EXISTENCE, AND HE ASKS HIMSELF:
WHO'S THE BABE IN THE RED DRESS?

NAKED RUNNING
(SEE BULLS, ANNUAL RUNNING OF THE)

NAMES, SIGNIFICANCE OF
IN THE BEGINNING WAS THE WORD. WHERE WOULD YOURS TRULY BE IF I WERE MIKE-IN-THE-MORNING? PROBABLY DOING DRIVE TIME IN SECAUCUS.

JOHN THE BAPTIST—WOULD HE HAVE LOST HIS HEAD IF HIS NAME WERE STEVE? I DON'T THINK SO.

NAMES, SIGNIFICANCE OF— ROCK 'N' ROLL VERSION

JAMES JEWEL OSTERBURG—WOULD HE ROLL OUR ROCK LIKE IGGY POP? AND SID VICIOUS—WOULD HIS CANDLE HAVE GONE OUT AT TWENTY-TWO IF HE WENT BY JOHN RICHIE?

NAMES, SIGNIFICANCE OF— SHAKESPEAREAN VERSION

SURE, BILL SHAKESPEARE SAID, "WHAT'S IN A NAME?" TELL THAT TO JULIET.

NAPOLEON

HE HAD PROBLEMS AT HOME . . .

I WAS THINKING MORE ALONG THE LINES OF POPULAR REVOLT, BUT, IN FACT, NAPOLEON COULD WELL HAVE BEEN FLEEING SOME BAD VIBES IN THE ROMANCE DEPARTMENT. HE DITCHED HIS BELOVED JOSEPHINE BECAUSE SHE COULDN'T BEAR HIM CHILDREN. COMPLICATIONS ENSUED.

NORTHERN LIGHTS (SEE ALSO AURORA BOREALIS)

THE AURORA BOREALIS AND THE NORTHERN LIGHTS ARE THE SAME THING.

NOSTALGIA

SOMETIMES I FEEL NOSTALGIC FOR A TIME I NEVER KNEW.

PAIN

SOMETIMES YOU HAVE TO LIE DOWN WITH YOUR PAIN. AS JUNG SAID, "THERE IS NO COMING TO CONSCIOUSNESS WITHOUT PAIN." SO LET'S GET CONSCIOUS.

PICASSO (SEE ALSO CREATION)

"EVERY ACT OF CREATION IS AN ACT OF DESTRUCTION." SOMETHING PICASSO SAID.

PLUMBING, THE ZEN OF

HAVE YOU TRIED THINKING LIKE A SHOWER?

POSSESSING THINGS

YOU WANT SOMETHING, YOU POSSESS IT—AND BY POSSESSING IT, YOU LOSE IT.

POSTAL SERVICE, SANCTITY OF

POSTMARKS ARE A LOT MORE THAN BUREAUCRATIC HIEROGLYPHS. THEY'RE SYMBOLS OF A SACRED TRUST. THAT PACKAGE HAS BEEN ANOINTED AND SEALED. LIKE KING TUT'S TOMB, WE OPEN IT AT GREAT PERSONAL RISK.

SOME PEOPLE LOOK AT THAT BOX AND SEE A BOX.

YOU KNOW WHAT I SEE? THE SPICE ROUTE TO INDIA! THE HEADWATERS OF THE NILE! THE DARK SIDE OF THE MOON! TERRA INCOGNITA. I SEE ALASKA, PEOPLE!

SO COME ON—WHADDYA SAY, LET'S BE A LITTLE HUMAN!

PREJUDICE

IF IT'S ANY CONSOLATION, IT ISN'T INSTINCTUAL. IT'S CULTURAL. IT'S LEARNED BEHAVIOR. SO THAT MEANS YOU CAN UNLEARN IT.

RECIPROCITY

IT'S AN ANCIENT CONCEPT. CONFUCIUS ONCE USED THAT VERY WORD TO SUMMARIZE HIS ENTIRE PHILOSOPHY. AND MUSLIMS CHERISH THE IDEA OF MUTUAL OBLIGATION. BY THEIR STANDARDS, IF SOMEONE SAVES YOUR LIFE YOU OWE THAT PERSON UNTIL YOU SAVE HIS.

BUT THAT NOTION IS HARDLY UNIVERSAL. CERTAIN NATIVE AMERICAN CULTURES, FOR EXAMPLE, BELIEVE THAT SAVING A LIFE—THAT GOOD DEEDS IN GENERAL—ARE A PERSON'S NATURAL FUNCTION AND THUS REQUIRE NO SPECIAL REWARD.

RELATIONSHIPS, DETERIORATION OF

PEOPLE NOTICE THINGS ABOUT THEIR SIGNIFICANT OTHER THEY DON'T LIKE ALL THE TIME—THE WAY THEY CHEW THEIR FOOD OR CLIP THEIR TOENAILS— IT'S A NECESSARY PART OF A REAL RELATIONSHIP.

PERSONALLY, I'M NOT INTO THAT, BUT LOTS OF FOLKS SEEM TO GET OVER THE HUMP AND KEEP FUELING THE DOMESTIC FIRES.

ON THE OTHER HAND, FOR ME, WHEN I BEGIN TO SEE FLAWS, CHINKS IN THE ROMANTIC ARMOR, IT'S A FORESHADOWING—A SURE SIGN, YOU KNOW—THAT LOVE'S ABOUT TO SKIP OUT THE BACK DOOR. ADIOS. FINITO, BENITO.

RELATIONSHIPS, ENDING OF (SEE ALSO LETTERS, DEAR JOHN; LOVE, LOST)

REJECTION IS ONE WAY TO LOOK AT IT. BUT WITH THE YIN/YANG, MAN/WOMAN THING, IT'S EITHER BALANCED OR IT ISN'T. IF IT ISN'T, ALL IT MEANS IS— IT ISN'T. IT'S JUST THE ETERNAL ECOLOGY OF THE LOVE THING.

REVELATIONS

A MOMENT OF INSIGHT INTO THE DIVINE NATURE? I GOT THERE ONCE.

IN PRISON. I'D BEEN IN ABOUT A MONTH. THEN ONE NIGHT, I CHUG-A-LUGGED SIX HITS OF POTATO HOME BREW WHILE WATCHING A STROBE CANDLE. I SEPARATED, DRIFTED UP AND CIRCLED THE PENI-TENTIARY TWICE.

SEX (SEE ALSO ALIENATION)

WITH SEX, THE OTHER IS GOOD. IT'S A TURN-ON. BUT IT'S A WHOLE DIFFERENT STORY IF YOU TAKE THE

OTHER FROM THE OUTER AND MAKE IT PART OF THE
INNER.

SHORT PEOPLE

SHORT'S GOOD. LOWER CENTER OF GRAVITY, BETTER
BALANCE. THINK OF ALL THE TOUGH GUYS WHO

WEREN'T GIANTS. BRUCE LEE. NAPOLEON—FIVE FOOT TWO AND HE CONQUERED EUROPE. ALAN LADD. JOHN WAYNE—THEY HAD HIM STAND ON BOXES. EDWARD G. ROBINSON. JAMES CAGNEY . . .

SLAM DANCING—IS IT ART?

INSOFAR AS IT REFLECTS THE SLAM DANCERS' INNER CONFLICT WITH SOCIETY AS EXPRESSED THROUGH THE BEAT, SURE—WHY NOT?—YES.

SNOW

SNOW USUALLY MAKES ME MELLOW—CURL-UP-IN-THE-CORNER TIME, SLOW DOWN AND SMELL THE FURNITURE.

SOULS, RUSSIAN, EXAMPLE OF

WILD BILL CODY HAD A RUSSIAN SOUL. DYLAN THOMAS. AL PACINO. DOSTOYEVSKI—SAME THING. HE GAMBLED AWAY EVERYTHING HE HAD.

SPEECH

DON'T TAKE IT LIGHTLY, MY FRIENDS. IF MUSIC IS THE PATHWAY TO THE HEART, AS VOLTAIRE SUGGESTED, THEN SPEECH IS THE PATHWAY TO OTHER PEOPLE. LIVE IN SILENCE AND YOU LIVE ALONE.

SPRING (SEE ALSO DEATH)

AH, SPRING, AND THIS YOUNG MAN'S FANCY NATURALLY TURNS TO THOUGHTS OF DEATH.

NOT DEATH LIKE "THAT'S ALL, FOLKS," BUT DEATH IN A CYCLICAL SENSE. SUNRISE/SUNSET, HIGH TIDE/LOW TIDE, THAT KIND OF THING. BEARS, WHICH WE'VE ALL HAD ON OUR MINDS LATELY, REALLY SAY IT ALL: THEIR DEATHLIKE SLEEP IN THE SEPULCHER OF THE CAVE, FOLLOWED BY THEIR AWAKENING REBIRTH. DEATH AND RESURRECTION— SOMETHING BEARS AND DEITIES HAVE IN COMMON.

POINT OF FACT: IN MANY CULTURES, BEARS THEM- SELVES WERE CONSIDERED GODS. SIXTY THOUSAND YEARS AGO, WAY BEFORE MITHRA, BEFORE THE BURNING BUSH, CHRIST, BUDDHA, WHAT DID OUR NEOLITHIC BROTHERS LIE PROSTRATE BEFORE? BEARS.

SPRING, EFFECTS OF (SEE ALSO BULLS, ANNUAL RUNNING OF THE)

SPRING SPRANG. WE'VE HAD OUR STATE OF GRACE, OUR GIFT OF SANCTIONED MADNESS, COURTESY OF MOTHER NATURE. THANKS, GAIA, MUCH OBLIGED.

NOW IT'S TIME TO GET BACK TO THAT ROUTINE OF DAILY LIVING WE LIKE TO CALL NORMAL. BUT BEFORE THINGS GET <u>TOO</u> NORMAL, A REMINDER TO ALL YOU PEOPLE OF THE MALE PERSUASION: CICELY'S ANNUAL RUNNING OF THE BULLS COMMENCES FIRST THING TOMORROW A.M.

STATUARY, FUNEREAL

UNTIL TODAY, WE COULD ONLY SEE RICK IN THE HAZY BLUR OF MEMORY. BUT NOW WE HAVE SOME-

THING TANGIBLE, SOMETHING SOLID THAT SAYS, "HEY, GUYS, IT'S ME, RICK."

IN SOME BELIEF SYSTEMS—JEWISH, ISLAMIC, CALVINIST—A MONUMENT LIKE THIS WOULD BE CONSIDERED SACRILEGIOUS. A GRAVEN IMAGE, A FORM OF IDOLATRY. LUCKILY, RICK WAS A UNITARIAN, SO I THINK WE'RE OKAY.

STAYING PUT

ARE WE HUMANS MEANT TO BE ROOTED TO THE SPOT?

NINETEEN SEVENTY-EIGHT. AUTUMN DAY. IT WAS LIKE SOME GENETIC CALLING. EVERY FIBER OF MY BEING SAID, "HEY, CHRIS, FOLLOW THE SUN." DID I LISTEN, PEOPLE? NOPE. I STAYED PUT. COUPLE WEEKS LATER, I'M PINCHED FOR BOOSTING RECORDS. THEN THEY STUCK THIS SORRY BIRD IN A CAGE WITH NO SWING AND NO VIEW.

NOW HERE I AM, YEARS AND MILES LATER, AN ALLEGED FREE MAN, ONCE AGAIN FACING ANOTHER BITTER, COLD WINTER. BUT AM I HEADING SOUTH WITH THE SUN? NO, I'M NOT. SO TELL ME—IS THIS GLASS RADIO BOOTH ANY LESS OF A CAGE?

STEVENS, CHRIS, ALLERGIES OF

WINTER'S ON THE LAM, NO DOUBT ABOUT IT. LIKE MY LATE UNCLE CYRUS, WHOSE ARTHRITIC KNEE UNFAILINGLY PREDICTED THE ONSET OF RAIN, YOURS

TRULY, CHRIS-IN-THE-MORNING, IS BLESSED BY ALLERGIES THAT HERALD THE VERNAL EQUINOX. YES, THE MARSH MARIGOLDS ARE DEFINITELY ABLOOM.

STEVENS, CHRIS, BIRTHDAY OF

JULY 3, 1963.

STEVENS, CHRIS, EXPECTATIONS FOR

I NEVER EXACTLY LIVED UP TO ANY EXPECTATIONS MYSELF.

STEVENS, CHRIS, HALF BROTHER OF

BERNARD AND I USUALLY CLICK, LIKE TWO HALVES OF THE SAME PERSON—LIKE SIMON AND GARFUNKEL, WOODWARD AND BERNSTEIN, SONNY AND CHER.

STEVENS, CHRIS, MEMORY OF

I CAN TELL YOU THE LAYOUT OF EVERY BAR I'VE EVER BEEN IN, WHAT THEY CHARGE FOR DRINKS, THE NAME OF THE BARTENDER . . .

STEVENS, CHRIS, OUTSTANDING WARRANT FOR

THAT WOULD SURPRISE ME, CONSIDERING THE ONLY OUTSTANDING THING I WAS EVER CITED FOR IN WEST VIRGINIA WAS MY ABILITY TO OPEN THREE BEER BOTTLES AT THE SAME TIME WITH MY TEETH.

STEVENS, CHRIS, SELF-ASSESSMENT OF

YOU KNOW ME—I'VE ALWAYS BEEN A STUDENT OF THIS LIFE, NOT A TEACHER. MORE OF A SPONGE THAN A FOUNTAIN.

STEVENS, FAMILY, FEUDS OF

MILLERS HAVE BEEN JAILING STEVENSES SINCE BEFORE THE CIVIL WAR. SEE, MY FAMILY WAS LIKE THE JAMES GANG OF WEST VIRGINIA. THE MILLERS WERE

THE EARPS. MY GREAT-GRANDADDY ONCE SHOT A MILLER IN THE NECK. DIDN'T KILL HIM, BUT HE WALKED AROUND THE REST OF HIS LIFE LIKE HE WAS LOOKING AT A PAINTING IN THE LOUVRE. IT'S BEEN US AGAINST THEM EVER SINCE.

STEVENS, FAMILY, HISTORY OF INBREEDING IN

IT CAN GET CONFUSING. YOUR THIRD COUSINS ARE ALSO YOUR NEPHEWS. AND IF THEY MARRY YOUR KIDS, THEN THEIR KIDS ARE YOUR GRANDCHILDREN, BUT THEY'RE ALSO YOUR THIRD COUSINS ONCE REMOVED. BUT US STEVENSES ARE ALL TALL AND OUR EYES AREN'T TOO FAR APART, SO WHAT THE HELL . . .

STEVENS, FAMILY, HISTORY OF INSANITY IN

NO. . . NOT THAT I KNOW OF. EVERYBODY WAS PRETTY NORMAL. FAILURES, BUT NORMAL.

TECHNOLOGY

MOST PEOPLE ARE AFRAID OF TECHNOLOGY. THEIR SOLUTION IS JUST TO FORGET IT.

THEY GET IN THE CAR AND THEY GO. THEY MOVE WITHOUT UNDERSTANDING. BUT YOU SHOULD KEEP IN MIND THE WORDS OF ROBERT PIRSIG. HE WROTE ZEN AND THE ART OF MOTORCYCLE MAINTENANCE. HE POINTED OUT—WISELY, I THINK—THAT BUDDHA

IS EVERY BIT AS COMFY IN THE GEARS OF A CYCLE TRANSMISSION AS HE IS ON A MOUNTAINTOP OR THE PETALS OF A FLOWER.

THOUGHT
THINKING'S WHAT GOT YOU INTO TROUBLE IN THE FIRST PLACE.

TRIBAL RITES
(SEE ALSO COMING OF AGE; CULTURAL RELATIVISM)
A NOBLE TRADITION. A MAN UNDERGOES A WRENCHING PHYSICAL ORDEAL, RECEIVING AN IRREVOCABLE MARK IN THE PROCESS, A SIGN OF HIS COURAGE AND ENDURING COMMITMENT TO THE TRIBE. FROM THAT MOMENT ON, CUSTOM HAS IT, THE INITIATE IS NO LONGER THE SAME PERSON. APPROPRIATELY, HE IS OFTEN GIVEN A NEW NAME, REFLECTING HIS ELEVATED STATUS AMONG THE PEOPLE.

TRUTH
THE TRUTH SLIPS AND TURNS, BUT THE FACTS REMAIN THE SAME.

VIRGINITY, LOSING ONE'S
I REMEMBER MY FIRST TRIP INTO THE REALM OF THE SENSES. WHEELING, WEST VIRGINIA, TRAILER PARK, NEAR THE SUMP.

I WAS SEVEN YEARS OLD. I KNEW AS MUCH ABOUT LIFE AT THAT MOMENT AS I'VE EVER KNOWN.

VIRGINS, CRYING

YOU KNOW, THOSE PAINTINGS OF MADONNAS THAT SHED REAL TEARS AND OFFER NO RATIONAL EXPLANATION FOR THEIR IDIOSYNCRATIC BEHAVIOR.

WHITE FANG AND BUCK

BUCK'S A MUTT—HALF SAINT BERNARD, HALF SCOTCH SHEPHERD. FANG STARTED OUT AS A WOLF IN THE WILD AND ENDED UP AS A HOUSE PET IN SANTA CLARA, CALIFORNIA.

YEAH. TAME TO WILD, WILD TO TAME, EITHER/OR. POINT IS, BOTH DOGS GET TO SEE BOTH SIDES. ONCE THEY KNOW THAT, WHO THEY ARE . . . DOESN'T MATTER WHERE THEY LIVE.

WILLIWAWS

THEY SAY IT'S AN ILL WIND THAT BLOWETH NO MAN TO GOOD. WHAT BETTER SIGN THAT THE WILLI-WAWS ARE ONCE AGAIN UPON US? YES, NEIGHBORS, THOSE UNSEASONABLY WARM WINDS FROM THE EAST. MY ADVICE: DON'T FIGHT 'EM. EMBRACE THEM. KNOW YOUR ENEMY.

WIND (SEE WILLIWAWS)

WILD, THE

WE ALL HAVE OUR OWN RELATIONSHIP TO THE
WILD. OUT THERE. OR IN HERE, IN OUR HEARTS AND
SOULS.

WINTER

WINTER. I CAN SMELL THE COLD COMING. I CAN ALMOST TAKE A BITE OUT OF IT. TASTES LIKE A STEEL BAR.

WOMEN, COPING WITH
(SEE ALSO GREAT QUESTION, THE)

WHEN THEY GET CHILLY, IT'S BEST TO JUST LET THEM RIDE IT OUT.

WOMEN, HOW TO HIT ON
(SEE ALSO ARCHERY)

I'D TELL HER SHE'S GOT GREAT LIPS.

WOMEN—WHAT DO THEY WANT?
(SEE GREAT QUESTION, THE)

ZEN
(SEE CARPENTRY; MATHEMATICS; PLUMBING; TECHNOLOGY)